/4 Days

D1708479

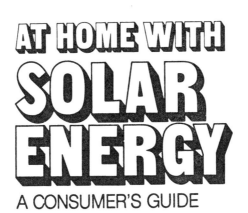

# AT HOME WITH
# SOLAR
# ENERGY

## A CONSUMER'S GUIDE

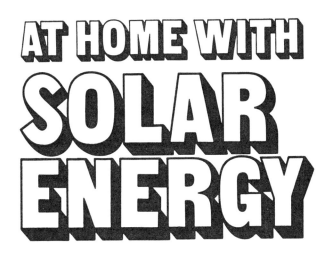

# AT HOME WITH SOLAR ENERGY

## A CONSUMER'S GUIDE

by

David Dvorkin

THOMAS NELSON PUBLISHERS
Nashville

*The author wishes to thank William J. Rose, who pointed out the need for this book, helped greatly to get the project underway, and served as a technical reviewer for the early chapters; Larry Preston and Art Adams of the Solar Energy Research Institute; Zomeworks Corporation; Harold Hay; Randy Dyer of the Solar Industries Association; many helpful employees of the Department of Energy; Marvin Yarosh of the Florida Solar Energy Center; and Polly Craighill, formerly with the Florida Solar Energy Center.*

**Library of Congress Cataloging in Publication Data**

Dvorkin, David
  At home with solar energy.
  Reading List: p. 180. Index.
  1. Solar energy.  2. Solar homes.
I.  Title.
TJ810.D87       697'.78       79-19370
ISBN 0-8407-5694-1

# CONTENTS

# LIST OF FIGURES

# LIST OF TABLES

To Daniel,
the brightest son in my life.

# INTRODUCTION

Western civilization—especially America, the most industrialized of all industrial nations—powers its machines with energy obtained by burning fossil fuels (coal, oil, and natural gas). Although it may come as a surprise to many readers, the energy we obtain when we burn these fuels is stored sunlight—the sunlight that shone on the plants that eventually became the fossil fuels, after tens of millions of years. We are now faced with the prospect of running out of these natural energy storehouses, or of not being able feasibly to mine them. This could happen within the next few decades.

Since we cannot wait millions of years until new fossil fuel deposits form, we must have alternative sources of energy within the very near future if Western civilization is to survive as we know it. The candidates most often proposed as the most important alternative energy source are nuclear fusion, nuclear fission, geothermal power, hydroelectric power, oil from oil shale, tidal power, coal gasification and liquefaction, wind power, and solar energy. Of all these, only the last uses direct sunlight as it reaches us.

By now you've probably heard about solar energy often enough to think it's at least worth knowing about. You've probably also seen enough conflicting facts and opinions on the subject to leave

13

you confused about what solar energy is, how it works, and what sort of potential it has. This book intends to clear your confusion.

Before examining the details of solar energy itself, this book will discuss (in Chapter 1) why the nation needs solar energy on a broad scale now. We will explain why the other proposed alternatives to oil and natural gas (listed above) simply won't fulfill America's needs in time. Solar energy is the only alternative that is safe, proven, and ready for use now.

Next you will learn how solar energy works in what is perhaps its most important use at this time, as an energy source for the individual home. You need not be either a home handyman or a mathematician. If, after reading this book, you decide to invest in solar energy for your own house, then you should find that the information and advice in this book will enable you to choose a manufacturer wisely, and to engage in any financial and legal negotiations knowledgeably. You will *not* need to build any equipment yourself; leave that to the many experimenters and inventors around the world who are hoping and trying to improve on the solar energy equipment manufacturers now offer. Nor will you need to perform any complex computations, as this book provides a number of simple and straightforward graphs to do that job for you.

Since the term *solar powered* is used with a special meaning by those active in the solar energy field, this book will use the expression *solarized house*, which means a house equipped with solar energy equipment. This equipment is also referred to as *solarized*, to distinguish it from the more conventional versions of such hardware. This terminology avoids language problems one occasionally runs across in writings on solar energy (for example, "solar-heated air conditioners").

Unfortunately, like any other booming business, the solar energy field is now being invaded by some unwholesome characters who are only after your money. Chapter 11 will tell you what to look out for and how to protect yourself against solar con men when you buy solar energy equipment.

Even if you don't want to spend money on solar energy (beyond the price of this book), the information presented here will interest you. If you do wish to do further reading on solar energy, you will find a list of the major books covering important topics at the end of each chapter. At the end of the book you will find a reading list on energy in general and solar energy in particular. This includes a one or two sentence analysis of each book listed. Also, at the end of the book you will see a representative listing of the major companies selling the equipment discussed in the book. You'll be shown how to obtain more comprehensive lists of companies, as well as sources for lists that are frequently reissued, with up-to-the-minute information.

Finally, in the Appendix you'll see a short list of major information centers to which you may write for still more information (pamphlets, etc.) on solar energy and related topics.

After you have read about solar energy and have seen what it can do for your house, the questions uppermost in your mind will almost certainly be economic: "Is solarizing my house economically desirable? Solar energy sounds like a good idea, but should *I* invest in it?" This book cannot answer these questions for you, but it does provide you with an understanding of the economic pros and cons involved so you can answer the questions for yourself. Chapter 10, on the economics of solar energy, contains graphs and text which, combined with an understanding of the physical principles behind solar energy (as explained in Chapter 2), should be enough to help you decide if and when to install solar energy equipment on your own house.

# SOLAR ENERGY NOW

It sometimes seems that an energy source must be the subject of a multibillion dollar government research effort, or produced and supplied by a mammoth multinational energy corporation, before many people take it seriously. Solar energy has been largely dismissed by the best-known energy experts as impractical or unworthy of serious consideration, or, at best, an option for the distant future. Even then it is endorsed only on a small scale. This chapter will examine the energy options experts *do* like, and will explain why the homeowner should consider none of those options as seriously as solar energy.

The root of today's energy problem is, of course, the energy crisis, with fuel shortages and the threat of future unavailability. If it were not for the energy crisis, there would be no reason to discuss solar energy or any other alternative energy source.

Most Americans trace the energy crisis to the Arab embargo on oil shipments during the October 1973 Middle East war. This embargo had an immediate and devastating effect upon underdeveloped nations who are not themselves oil producers. It crippled Europe and Japan. The effect on America was far less severe. But the grim fact is that the Arab embargo did not begin or cause the energy crisis. It was merely a warning—and a mild warning, at that—of what lies in store for all of us when fossil fuels run out. And they *will* run out: At the present rate of consumption, even

17

the vast oil deposits of the Middle East will be used up within thirty years.

Since the earth is not infinite, there can be only finite quantities of anything on or in it, and this applies to fossil fuels as well as anything else. Scientists have long used the word *fossil* to describe the remains of ancient plants and animals that have turned to stone, or "petrified," over a great period of time. (Actually, the remains don't really turn into stone: The process, sometimes called "permineralization," is actually quite complex and may take millions of years.) A famous example of this type of fossil is the petrified forest of Arizona. Another example is the reconstructed skeletons of huge prehistoric mammals and reptiles, collections of which can be found in most museums of natural history.

Fossil fuels are a different matter. Before man existed, dead plant and animal matter from the great forests and teeming animal life that covered the earth was slowly converted underground into coal, oil, trapped pockets of gas (natural gas), and a variety of related substances (such as the "oil" shales of the western United States, the tar sands of Alberta in Canada, or the peat mosses of the British Isles). Man now burns these plant and animal remains for energy to heat and cool his houses, to generate electricity, run factories, and move cars, trucks, trains, ships, and airplanes. But where did the plants and animals get this energy from in the first place?

Plants are natural solar engines. They use sunlight to convert chemicals from the soil and air into new plant material, building it into new branches, leaves, and roots. Animals eat this plant substance, using it both for fuel and as building material for their own bodies. Thus the energy represented by the plants, and used by the animals who eat the plants, comes from the sun.

Every gardener knows plant life is possible only because of sunlight. And every cattle farmer knows animal life is impossible without plants. This is what is often called the food chain, with plants at the bottom capturing sunlight and storing its energy in the form of plant material, and human beings balanced somewhat precariously at the top, eating both the plants and the animals

18

that eat the plants. It is obvious how we depend in this important way on the solar energy stored by plants. What is not quite so obvious, yet is just as important to modern man, is our dependence upon the sunlight that fell upon earth eons ago.

It is this ancient solar energy—captured and stored by the plants then alive and by the prehistoric animals that ate those plants—that man obtains when he burns fossil fuels to power his civilization. In the same way, the last summer's sunlight fuels our bodies when we eat a stack of pancakes made from flour ground from this year's wheat harvest. The important difference between fossil fuels and pancakes, however, is this: As long as the sun continues to shine, man can grow more wheat, grind it into flour, and make pancakes; fossil fuels, in contrast, are left-over parts of the ancient food chain, preserved and then changed into coal, oil, etc. by a series of fortunate accidents—and even then it took many years to happen. A combination of circumstances eons ago left us this storehouse of long-ago solar energy. Once we use it up, it will be gone forever. We have no way of duplicating within a short time what took nature so long to produce. Even if we tried, we wouldn't have enough plant material to do it with, since the dead plants and animals which became our fossil fuels piled up on forest floors for ages. Although fossil fuels are in a concentrated form which is particularly convenient for our use, their pricelessness (and our inability to duplicate the earth's store of them) really stems from the fact that they represent such a huge accumulation of dead organic matter, undisturbed by human beings over many generations.

Dead plant and animal matter is now piling up on forest floors and sea bottoms, but man is using it up much faster than it can accumulate—about two hundred times faster. In other words, by the evening of January 2, we have already used up more dead organic matter (in the form of fossil fuels) than will be deposited by nature during the whole coming year.

In practical terms, we are about to run out of fossil fuels.

As a result of the 1973 oil embargo, there was an economic slowdown in the Western world, which led to lower fossil fuel consumption. This created a false sense of security as to the availability of home heating fuel supplies. To add to this feeling of comfort, winters were generally mild in the first half of the 1970s, so home heating requirements were low. By autumn of 1975, however, the federal government was already warning the nation that the situation was critical; one severe winter, the government said, would quickly deplete our limited supplies of fossil fuels, leading to school and factory closings and cold houses. As if in fulfillment of that gloomy prophesy, the heavily populated Midwest and East have been hit by a series of winters that are among the most severe on record, both for the intensity of cold and their duration. The government's 1975 warning has come to pass. We have experienced critical shortages of heating fuels in the Northeast and emergency measures in the winter of 1978-1979 by the Defense Department, which contributed its strategic fuel stockpiles to the home heating fuel market. The rise of a hostile government in Iran, the world's second largest exporter of petroleum, simply makes matters worse.

Unfortunately, the attention of both citizens and government has focused on the severity of winters, as if that were the only important factor affecting our fuel supply. But air conditioning of homes and businesses accounts for almost 45 percent of our nation's energy consumption during hot months, and the amount of energy required nationwide for this air conditioning is increasing at the rate of 10 percent each year. Even if winters become mild again, a series of particularly hot summers could still do us in. (Most air conditioners are electric, so the power still comes from fossil fuels indirectly, since the great majority of power stations burn fossil fuels—in many cases, natural gas—to produce electricity.)

Estimates of just how much fossil fuel we have left and how long it will last vary widely, depending to some extent, perhaps, on the political philosophy of the person doing the estimating. However, here are some disturbing figures from reliable sources. At the *present rate of consumption*, America's natural gas will last for less than forty years, its oil for thirty, and its coal for more than two thousand. That doesn't sound too bad, but look at Figure 1 to see what has happened to energy consumption rates in

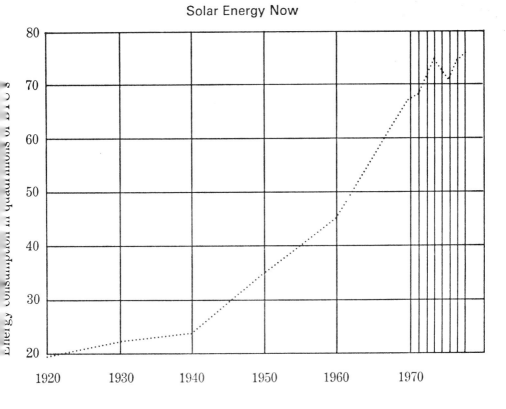

Solar Energy Now

Figure 1—U.S. Energy Consumption, 1920–1977
Source: *Collier's Encyclopedia*, 1979 Yearbook, s.v.
"Power and Energy Resources."

America since 1920. (The drop in consumption was during the recession following the 1973 embargo. After that, energy consumption rates returned to their previous growth curve.) Consumption rates will *not* stay the same. If they follow the present trend, we will run out of natural gas in twenty years, oil in fifteen to twenty, coal in about one hundred and ten. Still, one might argue, the coal will last beyond our lifetimes; in fact, U.S. consumption of coal has not risen as fast as our consumption of other

21

fossil fuels. But coal consumption has slowed only because industries and power companies have been switching from coal to other fossil fuels, such as oil. Now, as oil and natural gas supplies diminish and the price for what remains rises steadily, we see a reversal of this trend. Companies who can use coal and afford to convert back to it are switching back, lured by the widely advertised promise of low prices and a long-term, assured supply. So this means the consumption rate for coal is beginning an extended, rapid increase.

Trying to estimate what course the use of coal will take is difficult, but it is obvious that a large-scale changeover from oil and natural gas to coal on the part of American industry will significantly reduce the one hundred and ten years given above as the lifetime of U.S. coal. The changeover to coal (which does mean an energy supply for industry for the immediate future) requires that certain technological problems be solved, and it involves steep price increases—including a variety of hidden costs to the consumer. Recent newspaper and magazine advertisements by large energy companies boost the wide use of coal as the answer to our energy shortage. These ads imply that our domestic supplies of coal will be available at low prices ("if unnecessary government controls don't interfere," as they like to say). This book contends the opposite will be the case.

(The "energy companies," by the way, are the same outfits— Standard, Texaco, Exxon, and the rest—that we all used to call oil companies. Within the last few years, sensing where the money might lie in the future, these corporations have been buying up coal companies, companies that market nuclear fission equipment, and other companies in the energy field. The former oil majors are now the energy majors. We've been buying oil from them for years; from now on, we'll be buying our coal and other fuels from them, too.)

The 1973 Arab oil embargo showed us how dependent we are on oil, in particular on unreliable foreign sources of oil. Government officials and energy companies have since told us we can become energy independent. How? Supposedly by using recently developed technology to extract more oil from fields considered

22

depleted, by exploring new areas for oil and natural gas—especially at the bottom of the sea just off the nation's coasts (the "continental shelf"), by exploiting our vast coal reserves, and by a national *decrease* in energy consumption through conservation measures.

You should be skeptical of all rosy pronouncements from nervous politicians during an election year relating to impending big oil or natural gas strikes. Be equally skeptical of optimistic advertisements paid for by energy companies. Their motives may be a bit harder to fathom than those of politicians, but recent history has sometimes shown that the health, welfare, and prosperity of the average American citizen and homeowner are *not* the energy companies' chief concern.

One of this book's purposes is to help you protect yourself against those who want your money, with or without a fair return. Energy companies, despite the flattering things they say about themselves in their advertisements, all too often fall into that category.

Utilities are allowed to pass on to their customers the income taxes these companies owe the federal government. Your power company adds its taxes to the bill it sends you for the electricity and/or natural gas it supplies to your home. However, due to various tax loopholes and complex accounting maneuvers, power companies always pay far less taxes than they charge their customers for. Does this extra money get refunded to the homeowners "served" by the utility? Not on your life; it gets added to the power companies' profits. Meanwhile, their rates still continue to rise, because the various state public utilities commissions, which are supposed to keep power companies' rates under control, do not take this extra profit into account when they consider power companies' requests for higher rates.

The Environmental Action Foundation, which uncovered this astonishing situation, estimates that American consumers pay about $1 billion more in electric and gas bills per year than they ought to because of this deceptive and unethical practice. Furthermore, the foundation believes that a new tax loophole (thoughtfully provided to the power companies by our overly cooperative Congress) will result in the U.S. government refunding to these companies most of the more than $2 billion they have paid in income taxes since 1972. You can bet none of us will ever see any of this money (unless we happen to own stock in a power company!).

Let's try a less pessimistic approach to the question of future fossil fuel supplies. There is still oil lurking in old oil fields, and new technologies have appeared, and will continue to appear, which will enable us to find and extract this oil. There are also oil and natural gas fields we have yet to discover, and offshore drilling may well be one way to get at them. These highly probable developments will alleviate the problems of energy supply to a certain extent. The only problem with this new energy is the average citizen very likely will not be able to afford it. You've already seen your utilities bills go up; you'll see them rise even more in the future. Those utilities bills are the direct cost for energy; you're also paying some indirect costs, and those, too, are going up.

Although solarizing your house would reduce only the direct costs of energy, it is nonetheless useful and interesting to look at the whole picture.

Consider first the concept of *net energy*. Businessmen know it's not only the *gross*, or total, income of a business that counts, but also the *net*—what's left after all the expenses have been paid; in other words, the profit. A business that makes ("grosses") $1 million a year and, after expenses, nets $50,000 is obviously doing better than a business that grosses $10 million but has annual expenses of $20 million. The same applies to energy. We're not gaining anything if we use more energy to obtain a fossil fuel (or any other fuel, for that matter) than we can get from the fuel when we burn it later.

Modern mining is highly mechanized, as is the extraction of other fuels which are not mined. In addition to the muscle power of the miners, a great deal of gasoline and diesel fuel is needed to run the motors of the great array of mining machines used. Machines drill holes for explosive charges and roof supports; machines gouge the ores from the rock walls of the mine; machines load the broken ore into trucks and haul it to the surface; machines pump air down the mines for the miners. Similarly, the production of oil and natural gas requires gasoline and diesel fuel to run drills and pumps. After extraction, the raw fuel has to be shipped to processing plants. These plants, too, gobble huge amounts of fuel in order to operate. Finally, the processed fuel is shipped to the consumer, a step which uses still more fuel.

Great quantities of old fuel are required to get the new fuel, and all this old fuel, of course, represents energy. *Net energy*, then, is the amount of energy delivered to the consumer. It is the energy obtainable from the delivered fuel, *minus* the energy required to find the fuel reserves (coal seams, oil fields, natural deposits), mine or otherwise extract it, process it, and ship it. It is the "energy profit" of a fuel source.

In some of their recent magazine and newspaper ads, energy companies have argued that they need assured high profits so that they can afford to keep up their search for new fossil fuel deposits. These deposits are becoming even more difficult—hence more expensive—to find. This also means the energy required to find the deposits has increased greatly in recent years. Since the newly discovered fuel deposits are in parts of the world and at depths which make them relatively inaccessible, their extraction requires complex, expensive, and energy-gobbling technology. For example, to drill an oil well and complete it (which means installing the steel and cement hardware so the well is ready to produce) costs about $100,000 for wells in the continental United States. The same feat in the Arctic regions of Alaska, where production is now underway, can cost $10 million. And that's just for one well! The enormous difference in cost is due to the harsh Arctic conditions and the need to ship in equipment and to pay high salaries to induce men to go there. The same sort of economic problems occur in extracting oil and natural gas from fields previously considered to be depleted, the fields now reclassified as oil or gas bearing due to new extraction technologies. We are spending ever more energy to get fuels to factories, schools, and homes. But the energy that can be obtained from burning the fuels has stayed the same; it follows that the *net energy* of these fuels has decreased. The "need for greater profit" argument of the energy companies means the consumer must pay ever more for energy to compensate the energy companies for their increased outlays. So the direct cost to you, the consumer, tends to increase as the net energy of the fuel decreases.

But the increase in direct cost of the fuel does not entirely make up for the decreasing net energy and the increasing costs borne by energy companies. If the direct cost *did* have to make up for all this, then the fossil fuels would already cost more than most of us can afford to pay. How is the difference made up? By a wide variety of government subsidies to energy companies. These subsidies include leasing government lands (including the sea bottoms off the coasts) to the energy companies for exploration and production purposes at prices far below the value of these lands on the open market, and far below the prices energy companies would have to pay if they leased or bought the lands from private owners. The subsidies also include allowing energy companies to reap almost all the profit from the fuels extracted from these public lands. And the government treats these companies with excessive kindness at tax time (for example, the oil depletion allowance). The list goes on.

The importance of all these subsidies, open and hidden, is that the consumer pays for them in his taxes. The lower the net energy of our major fuels, the higher these subsidies rise, and the more the taxpayer pays.

A large part of the cost of clothing, cars, refrigerators, and other consumer goods actually goes to pay for the energy costs incurred by the producers, processors, and retailers of these goods. This even applies to food, since modern agriculture depends heavily on pesticides and fertilizers derived from fossil fuels—not to mention the fuel necessary to run the astonishing array of modern farm machinery. Thus a large part of the rising cost of living is due indirectly to the rising cost of energy, which is in turn due largely to decreasing net energy.

In brief, the lower the net energy of a fuel, the more you pay for it—if not directly, then indirectly, through higher taxes and a higher cost of living.

## Solar Energy Now

So much for the problem of our *current* major fuel sources. The other hope for the future touted by energy companies lies in the area of new developments: They promise us America's fuel problems will be solved by oil from oil shale, by coal gasification or liquefaction, by greater use of hydroelectric power, or nuclear fission. All of these are illusory or, at best, impractical, when viewed closely.

First consider hydroelectric power, which is obtained by building dams. Water from the lake behind the dam, as it falls over the dam face, is used to run electric generators. This method of generating electricity is excellent when first installed. However, almost all the good sites for large hydroelectric installations in the United States are already in use; there are very few places where new hydroelectric generating stations of significant size can feasibly be built. If you live in an area where such generating stations constitute the major energy source, you probably don't need to worry about an energy shortage in the near future. Unfortunately, all dams "silt up" in time; that is, silt slowly but steadily deposits on the lake bottom, until it eventually makes the lake into a mud flat, of little or no use in generating electricity. It will take longer for some of our major dams, but eventually all our dams will be made inefficient by silt deposits. When this happens, even those parts of the country where all or most of the energy is now supplied by hydroelectric installations will need to seek other energy technologies for power.

Getting oil from oil shale (a kind of rock formation impregnated with a waxy substance that can be heated to give off a sort of crude oil), and gasification and liquefaction of coal to produce natural gas and oil substitutes have all been proclaimed as major new energy technologies. But basic problems—technological, economic, and environmental—prevent these methods from becoming important in our nation's energy picture.

It cannot yet be shown that it is even possible to develop a technology that will produce energy from these proposed sources in useful quantities. Experiments so far have shown that if the required technology *can* be developed, it will be extremely complex. If these proposed energy sources someday prove practical, their net energy will be very low. And as we discussed before, that means you will pay high prices for that energy, directly or indirectly. Some estimates indicate we will use more energy to get oil out of oil shale than we will obtain by burning the resulting oil! If this proves true, oil shale will be a losing proposition, costing America more in energy than it returns.

Similar technological problems apply to coal liquefaction and gasification. No matter what we do to the coal after we dig it out of the ground, we still have to dig it out first. (The idea of converting the coal to gas while it is still underground and then extracting the gas the way we now extract natural gas has been around since before the First World War. Practically speaking, it has remained in the idea stage.) This has meant ever-deeper mines, with greater hazards to miners and greater costs to mining companies. This results in greater costs to the consumer, and means lower net energy for the coal.

The only other way of getting at coal that does not involve deep mines is strip mining. In some parts of the United States, particularly in the Rocky Mountain states, the seams of coal are wide and lie near ground level. The coal can be economically extracted by scraping off the surface soil and then digging out the coal directly. But strip mining causes enormous ecological damage: Along with the topsoil, animals and plants are removed and destroyed by great machines. If after the coal has been removed, the topsoil is replaced and fast-growing grasses are seeded, the cost of this reclamation is passed along to the consumer. As usual, you end up paying more for your energy. If the area is not reclaimed, much potentially valuable farm land has been lost. In this case, we are buying energy at the cost of our own future food supply.

Strip mining of coal can cause other types of environmental damage, all of them dangerous and expensive. Perhaps the most sinister of these is the problem of runoff. A variety of dangerous and highly acidic substances tend to leak or run off from the mine into nearby rivers and creeks, poisoning water supplies of cities and towns downstream. (The same problem results from the standard underground method of coal mining practiced extensively east of the Mississippi.) Here we see yet another hidden cost: The taxpayers in affected cities and towns have to pay for

28

special facilities to clean up the water damaged by runoff from the coal mines. Coal may *seem* cheap, but consumers still pay dearly for it in hard cash, indirectly.

The above problems apply to coal mining, regardless of what is done with the coal after it is extracted from the ground. Gasification or liquefaction of coal will not eliminate these objections. Any new technology that increases coal consumption only hastens the day when we will run out of it altogether. There simply may not be enough coal in the ground for a liquefaction and/or gasification industry to operate for very long, if coal should become our major energy source.

The same objections can be raised against oil shale. In addition to the potential net energy problems of oil shale referred to above, the techniques now proposed for extracting oil from oil shale require huge amounts of water. This means water will be diverted from farming, since the amount of water available in western states where most oil shale formations are found is limited. In fact, the available water in the West is even now the subject of fierce controversy between farming interests and new urban concentrations growing along the eastern face of the Rockies. Right now there is not enough water in that area for both farming and cities; imagine trying to find water for a new industry! Some underground water-bearing rock deposits ("aquifers") have been found in some areas of the West, but there is no reason to suppose they will be available to an oil shale industry. Even if such an industry could use aquifers for its own purposes, the techniques that use vast quantities of water to get oil from oil shale produce large quantities of very salty water. Salty rivers are already a problem in the West, so water generated by the oil shale industry could not be added to existing rivers without adverse effects on western agriculture and urban development. Injecting salty water into the ground raises the frightening specter of damaging underground water deposits, of which there are many in the West. If this happened, adverse effects on surface water would probably soon follow. Western states are already pressuring the federal government to guarantee they will be compensated for damage to agriculture and the environment, and

At Home With Solar Energy

for the increased social services that will be needed for new residents of their area, should an oil shale industry come to be. Who will pay for such compensation? In the long run, of course, you will. Here is another case of high indirect cost for what seems at first glance to be a cheap energy source.

The above objections have been put in economic terms, but there are also environmental problems. Protecting the environment is a real and serious matter, with aesthetic and economic ramifications. It has a real impact on all of us.

Until recently, the environmental impact of energy technologies was dismissed or ridiculed by energy companies. When it became clear the public didn't like the idea of filthy air and water and denuded landscapes, energy companies adopted the pitch that the choice is between energy and jobs: If we want a pristine environment, they argued, we will have to accept high unemployment and a stagnant economy. We must have high energy, they say, and there is no clean way to get it, because all suggested alternatives—other than the technologies they want to sell to us—are impractical, unfeasible, or far in the future.

Just how true these arguments are is a matter of passionate controversy, and this book will not take sides. But there are two other factors to consider. First, environmental damage means damage to your pocketbook, an idea introduced to some extent above and discussed at greater length in Chapter 10. Second, there is at least one energy source available that does *not* pose the awful choice between jobs and the environment.

Other new technologies that have been promoted are geothermal power, using superheated steam and water that gush from the earth in geologically active areas to produce electricity and to heat buildings; and tide power, using the tides to run electric generators. Here again there are technological problems. Tidal power may not be practical at all in any significant way. Geothermal power, which has been used for generations in some parts of the world (notably in Italy), has yet to be proved on the large scale required by our modern industrial society. But the biggest problem with tide and geothermal power is the fact they can be used only in limited areas of the country: Geothermal

30

power might someday make a small contribution to the energy needs of southern California; tidal power is practical only in a few areas. For practical purposes, most of the country can ignore these two energy sources.

The energy industry and the federal government are putting most of their faith in nuclear fission for the period beginning fifteen to twenty years from now and continuing into the next century. The idea behind nuclear fission as an energy source is simple. Certain substances are radioactive; that is, atoms within these substances are too large and unstable to stay in one piece. Every so often, an atom will split (or "fission"), shooting out a burst of tiny particles and energy in various forms, including heat. The particles shot out by the splitting atom may then collide with other atoms of the same substance, causing them to become more unstable and split, continuing the process. Under the right conditions, the process of atoms fissioning and then inducing other atoms to fission continues at an increasing rate, becoming what is known as a "self-sustaining chain reaction"—an atomic explosion, if the chain reaction runs loose.

If the chain reaction can be kept under control, the radioactive substance will not explode, and will put out a steady supply of heat. The heat is intense and can be used, for example, to boil water, producing steam that then can be made to run ordinary electric generators. For our purposes, the importance of nuclear fission is that it produces heat which can provide us with electric generating capability (in the same way we now use heat obtained by burning fossil fuels in power generating stations).

So far it all sounds quite appealing. By emphasizing the attractive features of nuclear fission in newspaper and magazine advertisements, energy companies managed for some time to spread acceptance of and enthusiasm for nuclear fission as a potential major energy source. Unfortunately, the matter is not so simple. Nuclear power plants offer attractive financial returns to the companies that manufacture their expensive, high technology equipment, and to the power utilities that install them as part of their power grids, but these plants offer little to the public except a significant danger, and still higher electricity prices.

At Home With Solar Energy

The battle lines over nuclear energy have been drawn for years now, with blandly reassuring power company executives on one side, and slightly hysterical environmentalists on the other. Such a situation makes a calm, objective appraisal of the matter difficult, since one must obtain data from the warring factions. The evidence seems to support the opponents of nuclear fission energy. The bland reassurances have been heard for years, and are still being heard, despite the bizarre incident at the Three Mile Island nuclear power plant near Harrisburg, Pennsylvania. At the end of this chapter you will find a list of some of the major books opposing nuclear fission, to counterbalance the heavily financed advertising in favor of nuclear power. A public opinion poll a few years ago indicated that almost seventy percent of those polled favored nuclear power plants. Over the years, attempts to block plants in various states by means of laws voted into existence by the public during statewide elections have failed miserably. The same poll showed the public is largely aware of the danger inherent in nuclear plants. Of course, the poll predated the events at Three Mile Island. At any rate, opposition based only on the scare factor will inevitably die out. It's important, therefore, to discuss other problems with nuclear plants.

Uranium is the usual fuel for modern American nuclear power reactors. Difficulties arise at the first point of contact with uranium—mining it. Dangerous gases are a problem in any sort of mining, but at least in mining nonradioactive substances, gases are normally kept below dangerous levels. In uranium mining, miners constantly breathe radioactive radon gas, and there is no such thing as a safe low level of the gas. Minimum exposure levels that *have* been decreed acceptable by the U.S. Department of Labor may not even be possible to maintain; if these levels someday prove possible, the cost of reducing miners' exposure to deadly radon gas will raise the price of the extracted uranium beyond anyone's ability to pay. The idea of living in a house where electricity is supplied by a nuclear power plant, at the cost of the lives of countless uranium miners, is surely a repellent one.

Remember net energy and its effect on your energy costs? Not only does mining uranium use up energy (like any other type of

32

mining), and not only will any attempt to reduce miners' exposure to radon gas use up even more energy, but *in addition,* uranium extracted from the mine must be extensively refined before it can be used by nuclear power plants. This industrial processing uses up still more energy. The refined uranium must then be shaped before it becomes the "fuel element" for a nuclear generator. This further processing decreases the net energy of the resulting uranium still further.

Coal mines produce acid wastes that threaten water supplies, livestock, and crops. Uranium mines produce radioactive wastes that threaten all life for anywhere from fifteen hundred to five thousand years, and mine wastes are easily carried by winds to areas far from the mine.

The reactor itself can be of a variety of different designs. But reactors have a few things in common: The efficiency of converting from nuclear radiation to electricity is quite low (much lower than for conventional fossil fuel power plants now in use); a certain amount of radioactive material constantly leaks to outside air and water; the plant is always on the verge of melting down into a hot puddle of radioactive molten liquid (tests of emergency systems designed to prevent such a melting show no one can design a dependable system); and government safety inspections of the plants often miss serious safety hazards in work procedures and physical equipment.

The near-catastrophe at Three Mile Island was not the only such incident, only the most widely publicized. Other reactors have reached the core meltdown stage, the worst possible stage, the one we are often assured is virtually impossible. (See the book *We Almost Lost Detroit,* listed after this chapter.) During the mid-1970s, an inspection disclosed that at one nuclear installation, the reactor had cracks in a pressure vessel. Had this not been discovered in time, the results would have been disastrous. Since that type of reactor was one of the most common in use in the country, many plants had to be shut down while their pressure vessels were carefully inspected for cracks. A shutdown is not a simple matter for a nuclear plant. Unlike a fossil fuel-powered plant, a nuclear plant cannot be simply shut down,

33

repaired, then started up again. Radioactive substances used in the reactor are so potent and dangerous, and their interactions so complex, the plant may have to remain shut down for years for even minor repair work. Imagine that nuclear energy boosters have their way; that America, by the end of this century, uses nuclear power for most energy needs. Then imagine that all plants using the most popular type of reactor—representing perhaps half of the country's generating capacity—have to be shut down for repairs for three years! Can we afford to depend on so unreliable a power source?

For technical, political, and economic reasons, operating a nuclear power plant requires that various deadly radioactive substances be transported around the country and stored until they lose their radioactivity. Transporting such substances through populated areas is enough to give one nightmares: A single train derailment, for example, could wipe out St. Louis or Chicago. The idea of storing the radioactive wastes until they are no longer radioactive is perhaps even worse. The period of time required ranges from hundreds to tens of thousands of years, and the wastes are so deadly that the method and place of storage must be absolutely foolproof and leakproof. We've only been storing these wastes for a couple of decades, and already, in certain storage facilities, great quantities of these substances have leaked away. (That's just what happened at the Hanford, Washington, storage facility.) If we can't take care of this deadly stuff safely for a mere twenty years, how can we possibly do so for two thousand years . . . or twenty-five thousand?

Transporting and storing radioactive materials around the country also introduces the most horrifying danger of all: the terrorist with the "suitcase" atomic bomb. Certain radioactive substances can easily be used by anyone with a little technical ability to make a very deadly, very dirty A-bomb. Just how easily was shown on a recent television special in which a college student designed such a bomb. All he needed to finish the job was the radioactive material itself.

Our society seems to have more than its share of alienated psychotics who dream of getting back at society for all their personal problems. The acts of sabotage, terrorism, and assassination these individuals and groups have perpetrated so far pale into insignificance compared to what these people could do if they got their hands on nuclear bombs. A madman might then take a million lives, instead of just one or two. With half a dozen countries now possessing nuclear weapons, with more countries thinking seriously of developing such weapons, and with all or most of these weapons watched over by nervous missile men and jumpy government leaders, a terrorist nuclear attack against Washington, D.C., or London, or Tev Aviv could easily set off World War III.

Terrorists need not even make a bomb. Some of these radioactive substances are so deadly poisonous, a single handful in a major city water supply could wipe out millions of people.

As the number of nuclear weapons and nuclear powers continues to grow, the danger of World War III increases, too. As the number of nuclear power plants grows, so do the opportunities for terrorists. The nuclear power industry admits it cannot account for all of the hazardous nuclear material it has produced. Where has the missing material gone? Is some of it already in the hands of terrorists waiting for the remaining amount they need to make an atomic bomb or poison a water supply?

Nuclear plants are so complex and involve such expensive materials and construction techniques, they can cost as much as fifty percent more to build than fossil fuel plants of equal generating capacity. Electric utilities have been able to manage this cost only by obtaining a wide range of subsidies from the government—subsidies for which you ultimately pay. The record of existing nuclear plants is dismal: Few operate near the electrical generating capacity for which they were designed, and many are shut down indefinitely because of construction flaws, safety problems, or, in some cases, uncertainty about future fuel supplies.

If nuclear plants are inefficient and costly, and if they deliver so much less electricity than they are supposed to, why are electric utility companies eager to build more of them? The reason is the usual one: money. The amount an electric company is allowed to charge homeowners for electricity it supplies them is based on the total amount of money the company spent building its generating capacity. By building a nuclear power plant that costs between one-half billion and 1 billion dollars, a utility company greatly increases its investment, thereby winning from the local public utilities commission the right to raise electric rates. The rates charged homeowners increase whether or not the consumer receives power generated by the nuclear plant—and even if the nuclear plant ends up not generating power at all! Since government subsidies at the beginning help the electric company pay for building the nuclear plant, and since various tax breaks help later on if the plant turns out to be a white elephant, the electric company actually bears only a small part of the total expense for the plant. The power company stands to lose little and to gain a lot. The only losers are the homeowners and taxpayers.

An entirely different way of getting energy from the atom is nuclear fusion. In fission, discussed above, large, heavy atoms, such as the atoms of uranium, are split ("fissioned") to obtain heat, which can then be used to boil water. In *fusion*, lightweight atoms, such as those of certain forms ("isotopes") of hydrogen, are made to join ("fuse"), releasing great quantities of heat in the process. This heat is used to boil water, which produces steam to turn electric generators, as in fossil fuel and nuclear fission power plants. The energy released in a fusion reaction is far greater than in a fission reaction. A fission power plant is a kind of tame atomic bomb; a fusion power plant is something like a tame hydrogen bomb. In every way but one, fusion power is vastly superior to fission power.

Instead of digging up radioactive substances for fuel, exposing miners to deadly radioactive gases, and exposing everyone else to deadly radioactive mining wastes, we could, in effect, use the oceans as the fuel source for a fusion power plant. The fuel supply, in addition to being quite safe to everyone who comes in contact with it, would also never run out. And the net energy of the electricity generated by a fusion power plant would be quite high.

Environmental dangers would still exist for fusion power

plants; there would still be radioactive wastes to dispose of. But these wastes would be far less in quantity and far less dangerous to our health and safety than those produced by fission plants; in fact, the danger would be from one thousand to half a million times smaller. Furthermore, the wastes from fusion power plants would be of no use to terrorists. Most of the danger that would exist with fusion plants would only apply to the earliest plants. Later versions of fusion power would almost certainly avoid almost all of these problems and would be far more efficient and considerably less damaging both to our health and to the environment than present-day fossil fuel plants.

If fusion power plants would have all these advantages over fission plants, why isn't fusion power boosted in this book as the answer to America's energy problems? Unfortunately, fusion power does not yet exist; it is still in the realm of theory. The advantages listed above will probably be associated with fusion power, *if* it ever exists. But at present it has not even been shown to be technologically feasible, let alone economical. By contrast, fission power, for all its disadvantages, does exist, and fission plants *can* be built. Technologically advanced nations, particularly the United States and the Soviet Union, are spending large sums of money on fusion power research programs, but we are still years away from being able to find how to use this method. If it does prove possible and economically desirable, estimates are that fusion will not make an important contribution to America's energy supply for fifty to one hundred years. We cannot wait that long for a replacement for fossil fuels.

Wind power, a technology promoted by some and ignored by most, may make a significant contribution some day, but, as with fusion power, the question is when that day will be.

Only one energy source has been proven technologically and economically feasible. The technology for this source is available, the fuel supply is abundant and endless, and environmentalists need not fear it. The source is solar energy.

The sun pours an enormous quantity of energy on us. In a quarter of an hour, the amount of solar energy that shines on

At Home With Solar Energy

earth's upper atmosphere equals the energy used by mankind in an entire year. A large part of this solar energy is absorbed by the air or reflected back into space and never reaches the ground. No solar energy equipment will ever use 100 percent of the solar energy that falls on it, any more than any other type of energy technology can ever achieve 100 percent efficiency. An astronomer who specializes in designing huge power plants that would convert solar energy to electricity estimates that even by the year 2000, when our nation's energy needs will be far greater than they are now, a solar energy system in the desert, built as a square one hundred miles on a side, would supply *all* of America's energy needs! The energy industry is discussing building fossil fuel power complexes almost this large to try to keep up with our growing energy requirements; yet this one solar energy installation, using only ten thousand square miles of desert, would be all our country would need. These figures demonstrate the quantity of solar energy available. However, there are sociological, economic, political, and ecological reasons why *individual* solar energy systems for individual houses are a much better way to use the energy from the sun.

One of the most interesting and appealing aspects of individual solar energy systems is that solar energy can be decentralized. Fossil-fuel powered electrical generating plants, fission power plants, geothermal, tidal, wind, fusion—these methods require huge central power plants that generate electricity, then send it to your home *via* a system of power lines. This means the homeowner is at the mercy of companies and government agencies that control the central power station and power lines, as well as the companies and government agencies that oversee the extraction, processing, and delivery to the power plant of the fuel the power plant uses. (This last item does not apply in the case of geothermal, tidal, or wind power; but these are also the least likely of all the above energy sources to have any effect on most readers.) In the case of foreign fuel supplies (e.g., close to half of our oil now), the homeowner is also under the control of foreign governments—in some cases, hostile ones. With solar energy, however, the homeowner is under no one's control, except for that part of his home's energy requirements that his solar energy equipment cannot provide—and this is usually not enough to make him helpless, should his supply of this nonsolar energy be reduced or cut off. With an individual solar energy system, the individual is relatively energy-independent. Healthy as such energy independence would be for the individual homeowner, it would clearly not be so good for the profits of energy companies or electric and natural gas utility companies. The decentralized nature of solar energy is perhaps its most politically important feature.

For years, energy and utility companies have attempted to convince the homeowner of the convenience of centralized power: Someone else does all the physical and mental work and worries about fuel supplies; you have only to flick switches and push buttons, and electrically powered servants do it all for you, everything from providing light to cooking your dinner and washing up the dishes afterward. All you do in return is pay your monthly utility bills. The recent spate of energy crises has shown just how reliable these people who are supposed to do the worrying and work for us really are.

But energy companies hope you won't see it that way, that you'll still want the dubious convenience of centralized energy. Since the conventional centralized power plants are running on fossil fuels such as coal, oil, and natural gas, they may not be with us much longer. So energy companies have started trying to drum up enthusiasm for oil shale, coal gasification and liquefaction, and nuclear fission. Though the companies in their advertisements try to present these technologies as ideal, discounting or not even mentioning the serious difficulties outlined above, they really know these technologies will require an enormous investment in money and energy and still give little energy. Energy companies aren't too worried about these stumbling blocks, for they have two great hopes: First, that through their advertisements they can scare the public into supporting them. Second, that no matter how great the technological, economic, and environmental problems blocking the initial development of these energy sources, financial support from the federal government, in the form of direct or indirect subsidies, can still bring one of these proposed fuel types to reality. This seems to be happening already with oil shale and nuclear fission development. With enough government money, open and hidden, pumped into the companies developing these technologies, the technologies will someday exist. The inadequate net energy of the resulting fuels will be taken care of by still more hidden subsidies and tax breaks. But that scarcely means the problems connected with these proposed technologies will disappear; it only means enough money will have been spent to cover up the problems. Those who use the new fuels will still pay, directly and indirectly, to compensate for impractical and inefficient technology; to cover the immense costs of extracting, shipping, and processing fuel and repairing the environment. It will be much the same as the direct and indirect costs discussed earlier in this chapter, only on a far greater scale. When the government makes an impractical technology practical by subsidizing it heavily to make up for its inadequacy, the money the government uses doesn't come from thin air: It comes from *you*.

One last criticism of our conventional fuel-powered civilization, a criticism that will apply as long as we continue to use fossil fuels, deserves mention here. Modern fossil fuel power plants, which provide most of the electricity to run our civilization, are horribly inefficient. Even the very best of them manage only a 40 percent conversion efficiency; the majority are closer to 33 percent. This means that, in the *best* of the plants, 60 percent, or three-fifths, of the energy locked in the coal, oil, or natural gas the plant burns is lost forever (mostly in the form of heat), instead of being converted into electricity. Furthermore, no matter what the efficiency of the power plant, a large part of the electricity generated at the plant—usually about 10 percent, and in some cases even more—never reaches the consumer, but is instead lost in the electric lines along the way.

So even now we waste an astonishingly large proportion of our irreplaceable supplies of fossil fuels. This is especially alarming when one considers that these fuels are the only source of the petrochemicals, plastics, fertilizers, pesticides, herbicides, and food substitutes on which our society depends heavily. If we use, at best, only two-fifths of these irreplaceable supplies for heat and electricity, wasting the rest, what will we leave our children and grandchildren?

By installing the proper solar energy equipment in his house—solarizing his home—and by decreasing heat losses through means explained in Chapter 9, the homeowner will in the long run save himself a lot of money. (For details see Chapter 10.) He will approach true independence from the effects of future natural, technological, or political disasters that might disrupt the flow of centrally generated energy. And he will make a positive contribution to the future, to the world in which his children and grandchildren will live.

*Additional Reading*

Clark, Wilson. *Energy For Survival.* New York: Doubleday, 1975.

Commoner, Barry. *The Poverty of Power.* New York: Bantam, 1977.

Fuller, John G. *We Almost Lost Detroit.* New York: Reader's Digest Press, 1975.

Halacy, D. S. Jr. *Earth, Water, Wind & Sun: Our Energy Alternatives.* New York: Harper & Row, 1977.

Hayes, Denis. *Rays of Hope.* W. W. Norton & Co., 1977.

Holdren, John and Herrera, Philip. *Energy.* San Francisco: Sierra Club, 1971.

Hoyle, Fred. *Energy Or Extinction? The Case for Nuclear Energy.* Salem, N.H.: Heinemann Educational Books Limited, 1977. The other point of view, as presented by a famous astronomer and cosmologist.

Lyons, Stephen, ed. *Sun! A Handbook for the Solar Decade.* San Francisco: Friends of the Earth, 1978.

Seortia, Thomas N. and Robinson, Frank M. *The Prometheus Crisis*. New York: Doubleday, 1975. Fiction: what could have happened in Harrisburg and Detroit. See also the 1979 movie *The China Syndrome*, which is closer to the truth than the nuclear industry admits.

Skurka, Norma and Naar, John. *Design for a Limited Planet*. New York: Ballantine Books, 1977.

# 2 UNDERSTANDING SOLAR ENERGY

The last chapter gave some idea of the enormous amount of energy that reaches earth daily in the form of sunlight and explained why the major energy source of our civilization—fossil fuels—can really be considered trapped sunlight. We cannot hope to duplicate this process to supplement our rapidly diminishing store of naturally produced fossil fuels.

What we *can* do is use the sun's light as it falls on us. Instead of waiting tens of millions of years (for plants to trap and store solar energy, for animals to eat the plants, and for both plants and animals to die and be converted to fossil fuels) we can install equipment in our homes that traps and stores energy from the sun, making it available to us as we need it. We can *solarize* our houses. This chapter will discuss how this is done. The discussion here is general, dealing, for the most part, with the basic ideas of solarizing a house. The details will be presented in later chapters.

The first important idea involved in solarizing is this: Sunlight is *not* converted to electricity; it is converted to heat and is stored and used in that form.

If this is your first exposure to the idea, you may be disturbed by it. You're probably used to electricity being the major energy source in your home; in fact, if you live in a new house, electricity is very likely the house's *only* energy source. There *are* ways to turn sunlight into electricity (for example, solar cells, discussed

43

briefly in Chapter 13), but none of them is economical now; nor is there likely to be a way that is, in the near future. The methods available to turn sunlight into electricity do so at great initial cost, placing them far beyond reach for the ordinary homeowner. The methods proposed for the future (such as "solar farms") for turning sunlight into electricity seem, for political reasons, unlikely to appear. Even if they are developed some day, they will be oriented toward centralized power systems. Chapter 1 explains why the homeowner is better off with a power source under his own control. Systems that trap, store, and use the sun's energy in the form of heat are the only solar energy systems available now that can be installed at a reasonable cost.

Our dependence upon electricity is largely a matter of convenience—the energy industry's convenience. Energy companies want a centralized power system because it is easy to control and profit from. This requires a system for transmitting the energy from the central location where it is generated to the users (homes, factories, schools, stores, etc.). For various reasons (mainly technological), electricity is the easiest form of energy to transport, in spite of the severe losses during transmission through power lines. Once it reaches your house, some of the most important uses to which that electricity is put require that it be converted into heat. This applies only in part to some of our luxuries, such as television sets, radios, record players, dishwashers, vacuum cleaners, and clothes dryers. These items make life more pleasant, but we can do well without them if we must. The necessities of life, though, use mainly the heat content of the electricity sent to our homes. It's easier to transport electricity than heat; in older homes, heat may be piped in, in the form of natural gas, or stored in a tank in the form of oil, but the idea is the same. What we really need is heat—and this we can obtain from sunlight.

(As later chapters will discuss, it is not practical to try to get one hundred percent of our heat needs from the sun. The amount it is practical to obtain in this way depends on a variety of factors, chiefly geographical location and local weather patterns. But sunlight can practically provide the homeowner with from twenty to ninety percent of his heat needs.)

Now that the idea of heat versus electricity is out of the way, let us consider how the heat of sunlight can be trapped, stored, and used.

There are two basic approaches to trapping, or *collecting*, the sun's heat. The first approach is to concentrate or focus it, and this involves *focusing collectors*.

The most familiar focusing collector is a magnifying glass (or "convex lens"), which generations of children have used to burn holes in paper, wood, and leaves. Light rays from the sun are, for practical purposes, parallel to each other. As shown in Figure 2, light rays falling on the magnifying glass are bent ("refracted") so they come together at a "focus" or "focal point." The temperature at the focus is high, because the heat energy of light that strikes the lens is concentrated there. (Only a small amount of the light's heat energy is lost by absorption in the lens itself as the light passes through it.) In Figure 2a light rays strike the magnifying glass perpendicularly in the first drawing, and obliquely in the second. If you tilt your magnifying glass so that light is not falling on it perpendicularly, the lens will no longer focus light to a sharp point, but will instead spread out the focus. This results in a cooler focus, which may be hard to burn anything with. This problem is important, as will be explained later.

Another type of focusing collector using the same principle as the convex lens is the "Fresnel lens." This is a sheet of transparent plastic or glass into which concentric circular grooves have been cut (see Figure 2b). These grooves refract light rays just as the curved surfaces of the magnifying glass do, so a Fresnel lens also focuses light to a point. As with a convex lens, sunlight must strike the Fresnel lens perpendicularly if the gadget is to focus properly.

Both the convex and Fresnel lenses are "refractors" because they bend light that passes through them. This means some of the heat energy of the light is absorbed by the glass or plastic lens. To

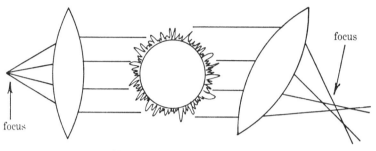

a. Magnifying glass (convex lens)

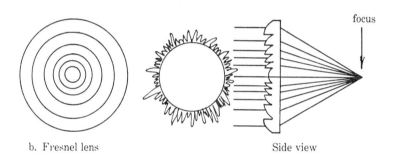

b. Fresnel lens                    Side view

c. Parabolic collector

Side view

Figure 2—Types of Focusing Solar Collectors

avoid this difficulty, most focusing collectors "reflect" instead of refract. Instead of bending light as it passes through them, the lenses reflect light from their surface so that light rays converge on a focal point without passing through the lens first.

What is it about the reflector that causes reflected light to come to a focus?

Figure 2c is labeled "Parabolic collector." A parabola is a mathematical form with a peculiar and useful shape. A mirror in this shape reflects light rays striking it so they all pass through the same point—the focus. This fortunate property makes reflectors feasible. The parabolic shape in Figure 2c is the side view of a parabolic collector. From the front, a collector may look like a circle or even—as in many actual applications—like a long, thin rectangle. In the rectangular case, the focus is not a point, but a line in front of the collector; this makes the rectangular design useful in special applications. The basic shape of a focusing collector of the reflector type need not be a parabola; other, similar mathematical shapes focus well enough for many purposes and have been used successfully by solar energy experimenters. It is important with reflectors (as with magnifying glasses and Fresnel lenses) that sunlight strike the collector head-on for good results.

You can buy a fairly good small magnifying glass at a reasonable price in a toy store—good enough for focusing light, that is. But look for a lens which is, say, six or ten feet across, and matters will be different. Even if you found a manufacturer with one in stock, you would have to pay a small fortune for it. Also, not much light would be able to get through it (a large diameter means a thick lens), and it would be extremely heavy. On the other hand, many experimenters have made their own reflecting collectors, using a variety of ingenious techniques, and at a reasonable cost. Homemade equipment is often of good optical quality (meaning that it focuses sunlight well), and in many cases the weight of the equipment is reasonable. So in the area of focusing collectors, *reflectors* are obviously preferable to refractors for large jobs, such as solarizing a building.

On clear, sunny days, a large focusing collector of the reflector type and of good optical quality, aimed at the sun, can generate enormous heat at its focal point. Temperatures of *thousands* of degrees have been attained this way in experiments. Such a collector, though less expensive than the large magnifying glass mentioned above, is far from free. However, for scientific work (such as materials research) where temperatures of thousands of degrees are frequently essential, such a solar apparatus is far cheaper than the complex furnaces scientists would otherwise have to buy.

Another possible application of solar energy that would require high temperatures generated by focusing collectors is the "solar farm." Versions of this idea have been proposed; this book will describe only the version that seems to have received any serious attention from our government.

The idea of a solar farm is to cover an immense area—perhaps in the desert in southwestern United States—with focusing collectors. High temperatures at the focal points of these collectors would be used to boil a liquid—possibly water. The resulting steam could then be used to operate electric generators, and the electricity thus produced could be fed to consumers through existing transmission lines. These collectors might well be like the rectangular ones described above since the focal "point" of such collectors is actually a line running parallel to the rectangle's long axis. The liquid to be boiled could be fed through a pipe running in front of the collector and along the focal line. The rectangular focusing collector is the natural one to use when a large quantity of liquid is to be boiled.

This sort of installation was referred to in Chapter 1, where it was estimated that a solar farm covering 10,000 square miles of desert could supply *all* of our nation's energy needs by the year 2000.

So much for theory. The fact is that the technology necessary for such a solar farm has not been developed; it may never be. Nor is there any evidence that the government and energy companies are willing to commit themselves to spend the enormous sums of money required to develop the technology to build a solar farm.

Nevertheless, if a solar farm is ever built, it will provide a major use for focusing solar collectors.

For the homeowner who is more interested in heating his house than in conducting scientific experiments on a 10,000-square-mile energy farm, the focusing collector is far from the best choice.

In each of the focusing collectors shown in Figure 2, the collector must point directly at the sun. This leads to two important drawbacks that seem to make the focusing collector unsuitable for solarizing a home.

The first drawback is the most obvious: The sun moves across the sky during the day. This means a true focusing collector must be equipped with a rotating base and some sort of driving mechanism so it points east in the morning and west at sunset, swivelling throughout the day to "track" the sun. A clock mechanism could be used to change the aim of the collector every few minutes. This way, the mechanism could be kept simple, and less expensive to buy, power, and maintain. But because the collector must swivel continuously to point at the moving sun, this reduces the temperature at the focus, and the efficiency of the collector. In addition, the sun's path across the sky changes with the seasons—it is higher above the horizon in summer and nearer the horizon in winter. So the tracking mechanism would need to be adjusted periodically to compensate for the changing height of the sun. Focusing collectors have a tendency to be fairly large, heavy, and cumbersome to begin with, and are vulnerable to wind damage. Add to this the weight of supporting and tracking mechanisms, and the whole apparatus becomes too heavy for the roof of an average house to support. There is also the matter of initial cost and maintenance: To focus properly, the collector must be well-designed and finely engineered. This means it is far from cheap. The tracking device must be powered and lubricated regularly, and worn parts replaced. It goes without saying that a good tracking mechanism is costly too.

In an understandable attempt to avoid the moving parts of the sort of apparatus described above, experimenters have compromised on cylindrical focusing collectors, which are basically the same as the rectangular focusing collectors shown in Figure

2c. These devices are installed with their longer sides facing east-west; this means they do not have to be adjusted to track the sun throughout the day, though they must be realigned as seasons change. Some ingenious designs based on the cylindrical collector advertised recently claim not to need realignment with the seasons. Temperatures these cylindrical collectors generate are not as high as the temperature at the focal point of a true focusing collector aimed right at the sun, but they are still high enough for use on a solarized house.

Thus the cylindrical collector avoids the high cost of tracking equipment, which needs lubrication, replacement of worn out parts, and power for the driving motor. It is still necessary that the cylindrical collector be of adequate optical quality—so even a cylindrical collector can be expensive.

Even the most ingeniously designed cylindrical collector requires *unobstructed* sunlight. On cloudy, hazy, or misty days, in fact, the performance of *all* focusing collectors drops to an unacceptable level. Even on bright, sunny days, focusing collectors do not use a large part of the available sunlight.

Sunlight is of two types: direct and diffuse. *Direct* sunlight is the familiar kind, light that strikes us directly from the sun. This sort of sunlight casts shadows. *Diffuse* sunlight, on the other hand, has been spread out, or scattered, and reaches us from many directions. On a cloudy day, the sun may be invisible, but we are not left in darkness: Light diffuses through the clouds, the sky glows, and you often cannot be more precise about where the glow is coming from than "above." On such a day, virtually 100 percent of the light shining on us is diffuse light, and we receive no direct light at all. On days like this a focusing collector, which can use only direct light, would be inoperative. But what about less extreme conditions—for example, less cloudy days?

Clouds are not the only cause of diffuse sunlight. Dust particles in the air may be invisible to the human eye, yet thick enough to scatter light. The same applies to pollution, haze, or mist, and even the atmosphere itself, since the gases that make up the atmosphere are made of molecules large enough to scatter light rays. So even on a cloud-free day, haze, dust, mist, pollution, and the air itself diffuse light. That is why, on a clear day, you can see an object that is in the shadow cast by a building or tree: Even though the object is shielded from direct sunlight, it is still illuminated by diffuse sunlight, the glow from the sky and from light reflected from the ground and nearby buildings. On a cloudy day, virtually all the sunlight that reaches the ground is diffuse; even on a sunny day, as much as one-tenth of the sunlight reaching us may be diffuse. Remember that a focusing collector cannot use any of this diffuse light.

One-tenth may not seem like much, but diffuse light becomes more significant if we look at the picture for the whole year. Studies show that of the total amount of sunlight received in a year in certain parts of Europe, half is diffuse; a study in Massachusetts found that two-fifths of the total annual sunlight received there was diffuse light; and even in sunny parts of South Africa (a generally sunny country) diffuse light is almost one third of the total sunlight received throughout the year. Since focusing collectors miss diffuse light and are able to use none of it, the numbers just given show a serious drawback for this type of collector.

A collector that could use both direct and diffuse sunlight would be able to use more of the available light on a sunny day than a focusing collector. More importantly it would be able to operate well even on moderately cloudy, hazy, misty, dusty, or polluted days—days on which the performance of a focusing collector would be seriously hurt.

Such a collector exists. It is the *flat plate collector*, and it seems to be the collector best suited for use on the individual home. A flat plate collector uses both direct and diffuse sunlight. It also tends to be a lot cheaper to buy and easier to install than a focusing collector. A flat plate collector *is* fairly flat, especially compared to a focusing collector, and it is therefore less affected by high winds. Almost all companies that manufacture solar energy systems for home use (see the Appendix for a list of these companies) design their systems around flat plate collectors. This supports the opinion that flat plate collectors are best for the home, and it also means a homeowner who wishes to design and install his own solar energy system has available a wide range of commercial sources of high-quality, factory-produced flat plate collectors.

A flat plate collector is kind of a miniature greenhouse. Like a greenhouse, the flat plate collector allows sunlight to enter, then prevents it from escaping. The light that enters the collector is converted to heat, which the collector holds. See Figure 3 for a representative design of a flat plate collector. In the drawing, A is a transparent cover (usually glass, sometimes plastic), which like the glass in greenhouses, allows sunlight to enter but will not allow the heat generated inside to pass back out. This is sometimes called the "greenhouse effect." It works because glass, though transparent to visible light, is opaque to the much longer wavelength radiation called heat. Area B is where the incoming light, having passed through A, hits an opaque surface (often painted black to better absorb light) and turns to heat. B's sub-

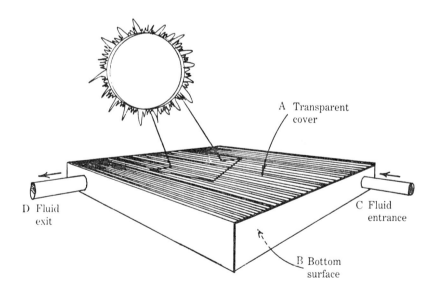

Figure 3—Simplified Flat Plate Solar Collector

stance depends on the specific design of the collector. For example, B might simply be a black surface; the space between A and B would then be filled with water made to move through the collector, entering at C and exiting at D, absorbing heat as it moves across the surface and carrying the heat to where it is needed. Air might be used in place of water, but the collector would still operate on the same principle.

A more sophisticated and practical idea is to have water or air circulate *through* B—through pipes built into B (see Figure 4a). A simpler version of the same approach—easier and cheaper to manufacture—is to attach pipes to the back of B (see Figure 4b).

Area A, the cover, traps the heat into which sunlight has changed after striking B. If this heat were not trapped, the temperature of B would not be much higher than the temperature of anything else exposed to the sun, such as the wall of a building. In such a case, the air or water used in the collector would not be hot enough to be of much use in a solarized house.

So one of the most important factors in determining the efficiency of a flat plate solar collector is the rate at which it loses heat to the surrounding air, compared to the rate at which it gains heat from the sun. Heat loss is unavoidable, but there must be a wide margin of heat gain over loss if the collector is to function well. The collector must raise the air or water (the "working fluid") to a sufficiently high temperature so that the fluid can be used in the house. The cover, A in Figure 3, raises the efficiency of the flat plate collector by reducing the device's heat loss.

There are two drawbacks to the use of the cover. First, whether A is glass or plastic, it is not completely transparent to visible light. Less than 100 percent of the light striking one side of A actually gets through to the other side. A's surfaces reflect some light, and the material from which A is made absorbs some light. With good quality glass there is not much difficulty with absorption, but reflection will cut down on the light passing through A by about eight percent. Sometimes a double cover is used for extra heat retention, but this means an eight percent reduction in light reaching B for *each* of the covers. These effects cannot be eliminated. Trying to reduce them significantly leads to

53

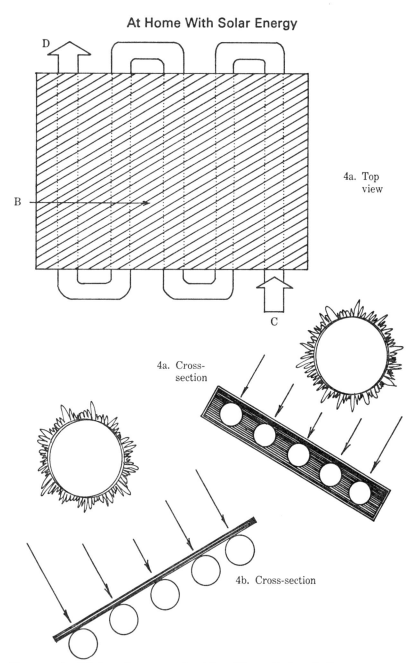

4a. Top view

4a. Cross-section

4b. Cross-section

Figure 4—Piping System of a Flat Plate Solar Collector

using expensive materials (special plastics, specially treated glass) and this raises the price of the collector unit.

The other drawback involved in the use of a cover is breakability. Glass breaks. The problem can be somewhat alleviated by using special plastics or special glass, but this means raising the price of the unit. Experimenters are investigating a variety of special plastics and glasses, searching for one that will be strong and highly transparent and, at the same time, reasonably priced. So far their search has not turned up anything satisfactory. Most individuals and companies oriented toward immediate practical applications of solar energy seem to feel the homeowner is better off using good glass of fairly good optical quality, but not a very expensive variety. The idea is that the moderately reduced efficiency of the solar collector with less than perfectly transparent glass (and also the cost of occasionally replacing broken glass covers) will, in the long run, cost the homeowner less than buying more exotic varieties of glass or plastic. Glass, though more breakable than plastic, is cheaper than plastics that would be used as collector covers, and it weathers extremely well. So this is an argument for using glass rather than plastic, and for using ordinary glasses rather than exotic, expensive ones.

Chapter 1 discussed the energy used by industry to *produce* energy, and to run factories, stores, etc.; this was part of the discussion of "net energy." Energy is expended to find and extract (for instance) oil, transport it, refine it, and ship it to customers; similarly, energy is expended to find and extract iron or aluminum, or plastic (which, by the way, is made from crude oil). Not only does it take energy to supply energy, but it also takes energy to supply materials from which products we buy are made.

Just as some energy sources require more energy to exploit them, so do some materials require more energy than others, because they are harder to find, have to be transported further, or because the industrial process of preparing the material for factory use requires a great deal of energy.

Take aluminum, for example; extracting it from raw ore and converting the result into the familiar metal gobbles huge amounts of energy. (This means "fresh" aluminum is fairly expensive, which is why some breweries now find it cheaper to buy back old beer cans and use them as raw material for new beer cans, rather than buying new aluminum.) Wood, on the other hand, has cost society very little in terms of energy by the time it reaches us in finished products. To an extent, the same is true of glass (most of the raw material for glass is sand!).

Environmentalists like to rate different materials in terms of their *energy intensiveness*—the total amount of energy that goes into finding, extracting, processing, and shipping the material. The energy intensiveness of aluminum is very high (which is bad); the energy intensiveness of wood is very low (very good); and that of ordinary glass is fairly low (fair).

Like energy sources with low net energy, materials with high energy intensiveness represent a very real cost to all of us—a social and environmental cost that eventually shows in higher taxes and a higher cost of living. We don't *see* energy intensiveness represented in products we buy, just as we don't *see* the net energy of energy sources we pay for. Hidden subsidies and tax breaks to the industries involved even out the prices, making these materials competitive with materials of lower energy intensiveness, and making the energy sources competitive with energy sources with higher net energy. But this competitiveness is artificial, because subsidies and tax breaks all come out of our pockets in the long run. So it is in our best interests to buy products with low energy intensiveness, and to try to use energy sources with high net energy.

In sum, solar collectors made of wood and ordinary glass are preferable—in a broad, social context—to those made of exotic plastics or special glasses, or those with frames made of materials more energy intensive than wood. Table 1 shows the energy intensiveness of a variety of materials. Values are given in terms of the energy intensiveness of sand and gravel, given as 1.

Some manufacturers and experimenters use substances such as aluminum rather than wood, in spite of the higher energy intensiveness, because of a weight advantage. For a solar collector system designed for the roof of a house, there is an obvious

Table 1. Energy Intensiveness of Basic Materials.

| Sand and gravel (cement) | 1 |
|---|---|
| Coal | 2 |
| Cement | 110 |
| Inorganic chemicals | 130 |
| Plastics | 140 |
| Paper | 300 |
| Finished plate glass | 340 |
| Steel | 600 |
| Lead | 615 |
| Zinc | 700 |
| Copper | 1,000 |
| Electrically processed metals | 2,440 |
| High-grade steel alloys (silicone and metal) | 2,820 |
| Aluminum | 3,200 |
| Titanium | 6,720 |

Notes

1. The energy intensiveness of wood can not be given since it depends too heavily on the type of wood.
2. These figures include energy required for production, use of manufacturing equipment, and transportation of finished goods. The energy used in finding ores or other raw supplies, mining those ores, and shipping them to industrial centers where a useful substance is extracted varies greatly for each substance listed. This depends on the location of the ore and the processing centers, and similar factors. So these figures may vary greatly. But such high energy intensive materials as aluminum and titanium are harder and more expensive to find and process than the substances at the beginning of the list. If energy involved in finding and processing the ores were included, the disparity between the top of the table and the bottom would be even greater. Table is adapted from *Energy for Survival*, by Wilson Clark. © 1974 Wilson Clark. Used by permission of Doubleday and Company, Inc.

advantage to making the system as light as possible. A homeowner would be understandably upset if the solar collectors placed on his roof ended up in his living room. (The relation between collector weight and house design will be discussed in Chapter 7).

It has been shown that the cover, A in Figure 3, increases the efficiency of a solar collector by decreasing the amount of heat lost from the collector. The efficiency of the collector can also be increased by improving the performance of surface B—making it retain more of the heat generated by the light striking it. An interesting approach to this is the "selective surface." This involves coating B with substances that allow B to absorb heat from incoming sunlight, but lessen the amount of heat that radiates away from B. B then becomes a "selective surface." Unfortunately, the substances used to coat B to make it "selective" are expensive, and the coating must be applied precisely. Selective surfaces are expensive now, and will not become widely used until and unless their cost decreases. Such a change, unfortunately, is not in sight. The selective surface is just entering the commercial production stage. But the potential effect of the selective surface on the performance of solar collectors is significant, and the reader thinking seriously of adding a solar energy system to his home should know what the term *selective surface* means.

Focusing collectors must be aimed directly at the sun to achieve optimum results; this is a major drawback to their use. Even flat plate collectors must be properly aimed for best results, but in their case, the aim does not have to change throughout the day. A flat plate collector is mounted facing south in the Northern Hemisphere, north in the Southern Hemisphere. In other words, it faces the equator. Since the sun rises quite a bit above the horizon during the day, the collector actually tilts backward from vertical, with the amount of tilt decreasing with distance from the equator. The closer to the North Pole the house is located, the closer to vertical the collector should be. As shown in Figure 5 angle "A" is larger at higher latitudes. Many feel that, for best results, the collector's tilt should be changed twice a year to compensate for the changing height of the sun's path across the sky. This is the same as saying angle "A" should be changed; the figure usually given for "A" is latitude plus fifteen degrees during winter, and latitude minus fifteen degrees during summer. So the collector is tilted back during summer, when the sun is higher, and forward during winter, when the sun is lower. This is discussed further in Chapter 8. Except for the adjustment for latitude (a one-time-only matter) and the twice-yearly adjust-ment for season (if one wants optimal results), the flat plate collector needs no further corrections.

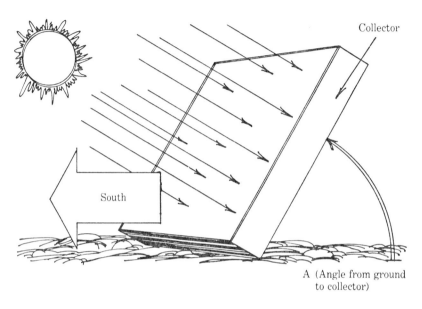

A (Angle from ground to collector)

Figure 5—Orientation of a Flat Plate Collector to the Sun

Important as the collector system is, it is only half of a solar energy system. Once the sun's heat has been collected, it must be transported to parts of the house where it is needed. It must also be stored somewhere, so heat will be available at night and on very cloudy days.

The description of flat plate collectors mentioned the working fluid (normally air or water) that moves through the collector, or through pipes built into the collector. This fluid absorbs heat generated in the collector. The collector allows the sun to heat the working fluid, which in turn is pumped through pipes, carrying heat to where it's needed.

The homeowner examining solar energy equipment must choose between systems that use air or water as the working fluid. The choice of working fluid also determines the storage

59

method used in the solar energy system. This fact has influenced some people to choose water-based systems. Water can absorb a lot of heat quickly, and a small amount of water can hold a great deal of heat. This means water circulating through a flat plate collector can absorb heat in the collector well enough to be practical. It also means the heated water can be pumped into a tank built underground, where it then acts as the storage medium for collected heat. (The tank does not have to be built underground, but it is good practice to do so, for the surrounding earth insulates the water. See Figure 6 for a simplified picture of a water-based system.) The volume of water moving through the pipes at a given time need not be excessively large, because of the amount of heat the water can hold. This means that the pipes can be of reasonable size, and the pump that keeps the water moving need not be large or expensive to operate.

If air is used as the working fluid, a much larger volume will be required to hold a comparable amount of heat. The amount of air moving through the system to transport heat from the collector to the house will be very large, as will be the storage location. This means large air ducts and a fan considerably more powerful than the pump used in a water-based system. So an air-based system will consume considerably more operating fuel. (The fan in a small solar energy system is typically in the range of one half to one horsepower.) Also, the storage tank cannot simply be filled with hot air, because it would have to be enormous to hold enough heat. This is because air holds much less heat than water.

Yet the picture is not as one-sided in favor of water-based systems as the above might make it seem.

The problem of a huge storage tank for air can be avoided by using something other than air to store heat—something that requires much less room than air, but still lets air heat it. What would fit the bill? A widely used substance is rock: A storage tank is filled with rocks, and hot air from the collector is circulated between the rocks, transferring heat from the air to the rocks. The rocks should be smooth, round, and about the same size, so hot air coming from the solar collector can move freely through the tank, contacting all the rocks. Rocks of the type described

60

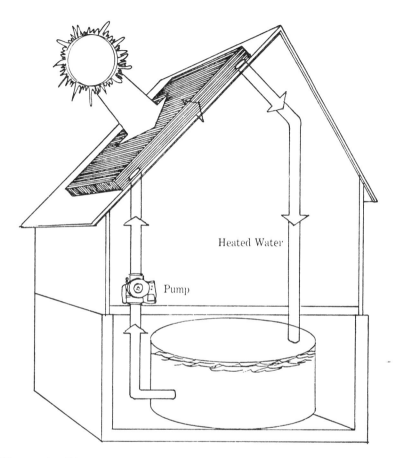

Figure 6—Simplified Water-Based Solar Energy Collection and
Storage System

above can be found along the bottoms of old riverbeds. See Figure
7 for a simplified picture of a hot-air-rock system.

Even with rocks for heat storage, the air-based system still has
the disadvantage of requiring large air ducts and a powerful
pump. However, this is largely outweighed by four drawbacks to
the water-based system: freezing, scaling, corrosion, and leakage.

Water freezes at thirty-two degrees Fahrenheit at sea level,

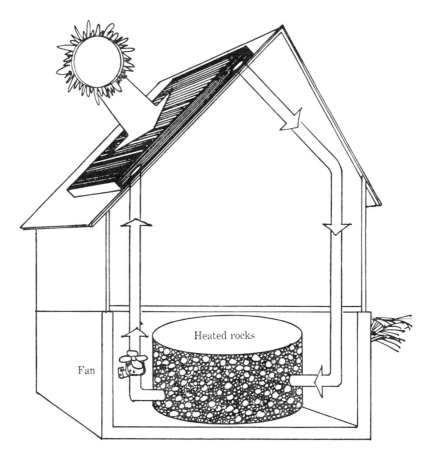

Figure 7—Simplified Air-Based Solar Energy Collection and Storage System (Using Rocks)

and at slightly lower temperatures at higher altitudes. In winter, when the heat collected by the solar energy system is most needed in the house, frozen water in the system's pipes can render the system inoperative—an unpleasant surprise for the homeowner who shelled out a few thousand dollars to solarize his home. Some water-based systems on the market try to get around this difficulty, but the cure can be worse than the disease. One system drains water from the collector and exposed piping at night and stores it away from the cold. This means extra controls and extra expense, and it also increases the number of places in the system where a mechanical breakdown can occur. Other systems use a combination of water and substances much like automobile antifreeze for the working fluid; some use fluids other than water. Again, antifreeze or a water substitute increase the price significantly. This higher price shows up again if the working fluid should some day leak out and have to be replaced. There is a related problem, a potentially dangerous one, when the system is used to heat water and a living area. More on this in Chapter 3.

Water corrodes parts of a water-based system and deposits mineral scale throughout the system. Corroded and scaled parts must be replaced or repaired, at a significant maintenance cost. The usual way to avoid this increased cost is to pay more at the beginning: by using distilled water, and buying a system that can withstand corrosion. This all means more expensive materials. One ingenious system on the market is made of materials that expand, contract, and flex with changing temperatures and the natural slight movements of a house. This action is said to break up scale deposits and eliminate that problem. Problems of cost and maintenance are not mentioned in the advertising; if this system becomes popular, it will be possible to say something more conclusive about it, because a statistical base will be available.

Similar cost problems apply to leakage. The more water-tight the pipes and connections must be, the more expensive they are to buy and install. Actually, 100 percent water-tightness is not practical, but the only alternative to it is constant replenishment of water. This is a bother, and if anything other than tap water is used in the system, it becomes an expensive chore, too. Leakage also occurs with air-based systems, but it is not a problem: With a leaking air-based system, you do not have to worry about replacing the working fluid; but your system's effectiveness is reduced by loss of heated air.

With air as a working fluid, the advantage of not having to worry about freezing, scaling, corrosion, or leakage outweighs the disadvantages of a bigger pump and larger ducts—if the solar energy system is to be used primarily to heat a home. For other applications of solar energy in the home, the picture is not so simple, as will be discussed later.

For years, experimenters have been working on a heat storage system that shows real promise, but is still beset by severe problems. This storage method is called "eutectic salts," or "salts of fusion." These salts are substances that melt when exposed to heat, absorbing a great deal of heat as they do so. Later, when they resolidify, the salts give off heat again. The amount of heat involved is very large, which explains the effort and time experimenters have spent designing and building eutectic salt heat storage devices. One such salt (Glauber's Salt) will store heat five times as well by weight as water, and twenty-five times as well by weight as rocks. (The precise numbers involved with these salts vary quite a bit from one book to another, because the numbers have been derived from different studies, and because the amount of heat stored by water and rock changes with conditions such as changing temperatures.)

It is a fact that eutectic salts can store much heat; unfortunately, the problems standing in the way of their wide use are large, too. The salts, after they have melted and resolidified a few times, tend to form crystals. Once these crystals have formed, they do not melt, and so do not take part in the process of heat storage and release. As more salt crystallizes in the tank, less is available for heat storage. After a time the storage device becomes virtually useless, as it can no longer store enough heat to fill its role as part of a solar energy system. Another problem is the expense of buying eutectic salts in the first place. Presumably, if salt storage systems became popular (which would require solving the crystallization problem), the price of the salts would fall.

Some ingenious experimenter might solve the crystallization problem next week, and large-scale production of eutectic salt heat storage devices for solarized homes might then begin, bringing the price of an individual unit down, and making ready-made, efficient heat storage systems widely available. But it's just as likely none of this will happen.

The point of this discussion is that both water-based solar energy systems using water for heat storage and air-based systems using rocks for heat storage are now commercially available from reputable solar energy companies, and it is to these systems (preferably air-based systems) that the homeowner who is considering solarizing his house should look. Interesting and promising as many of the experimental systems may be, it would be foolish to ignore working systems now available and gamble on hoped-for technological breakthroughs.

Preceding illustrations have shown the collector on the roof of a house and the heat storage tank in the ground beneath it (or in the basement). This is a space-saving approach, but is not the only one, and in many cases not the best one. The solar equipment can be free-standing, as in Figure 8, with pipes to carry hot air or water to the house and back to the tank after use. This requires

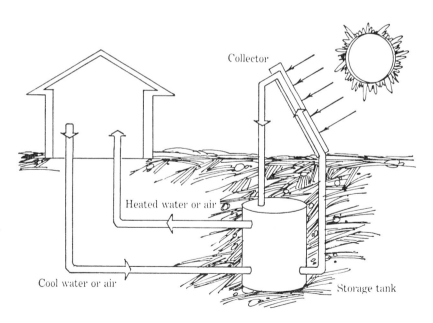

Figure 8—Solar Energy System with Free-Standing Collector and Free-Standing Heat Storage Tank

65

more land, but if land is available, the free-standing solar system may be better in some cases. Solarizing an existing house can be a difficult job, for reasons discussed in Chapter 7; the concerns in such a case are with the weight of the collector on the roof, fitting pipes into the house, and filling much of the basement with the heat storage tank or digging a large hole under the basement floor to hold the tank. The free-standing system bypasses these difficulties.

Another problem that will be discussed further in later chapters is shadow falling from trees or neighboring buildings on the collector. A free-standing collector would be best here, too. The roof of an existing house may be in shade for much of the day, but part of the grounds around the house may have adequate sunlight for a free-standing solar collector unit.

For free-standing collectors used to heat swimming pools, the storage system is the water in the swimming pool itself! In a clever use of free-standing collectors, a row of collector units was made to form a fence along the south side of a house, thus serving two roles at once.

Free-standing collectors permit some ingenious designs. The primary disadvantage is that a free-standing collector (or a free-standing storage tank) requires many extra feet of piping. Integrating both units with the body of a house has the advantage of compactness, including less piping. This method is particularly attractive in the case of a house still in the design stage, since design modifications to include the solarizing system can mean significant savings in initial construction and subsequent heating and cooling of the house. This is discussed further in Chapters 6 and 7.

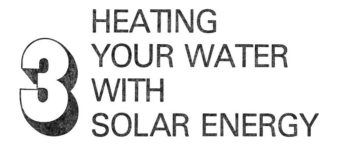

# HEATING
# YOUR WATER
# WITH
# SOLAR ENERGY

Among the many hidden costs of running a house is money paid for energy required to heat water. Think of all the ways hot water is used in the home—for baths, showers, washing dishes, and washing clothes. Unlike space heating, which is needed only in winter, or air conditioning, needed only in summer, hot water is needed all year. In the long run, this adds up to a fair amount of money. According to one estimate, the average American family requires ten thousand kilowatt-hours of electricity per year just to heat water for home use. To estimate how much you pay each year for water heating, ask your local electric company how much you pay for a kilowatt-hour of electricity, then multiply that amount by ten thousand.

To generate one kilowatt-hour of electricity, the electric company must burn about one pound of coal. Therefore, just *one* typical home in America requires mining and burning ten thousand pounds (five tons) of coal per year merely to provide hot water for baths, etc.

For houses equipped with gas water heaters, the above figures must be modified somewhat. Assuming the total yearly energy requirement for water heating is the equivalent of ten thousand kilowatt-hours of electricity, that the efficiency of a water heater is 60 percent, and that the natural gas being supplied to a house has an energy content of three-tenths kilowatt-hours of electricity per cubic foot, you can calculate that the average house with a gas water heater uses almost fifty-seven thousand cubic feet of natural gas each year to heat water. If you can find out how much you pay for a cubic foot of natural gas, you can determine your yearly energy bill for hot water by multiplying the cost per cubic foot by fifty-seven thousand.

According to one estimate, the average American family spends 15 percent of its annual energy bill just to heat water!

Of all the ways energy is used in the home, heating water is the most attractive candidate for solar energy. It is relatively easy and economically rewarding to heat water for home use with solar energy, rather than with natural gas or electricity supplied by a local utility company.

Solar water heating has been in wide use throughout the world for many years. Solar water heaters have been very popular in Japan, Israel, Australia, and, in our own country, in Florida and Southern California. Note that these are areas which receive much sunshine, and have populations accustomed to a high (Western) standard of living. Solar water heating is useful not only in areas where the average person uses much less hot water than the average American, but also in those parts of the world where families are used to an "American" style of life.

It is of particular interest to note that solar water heaters are less popular in Japan, Australia, and the United States than they were years ago. The basic reason for this decline is the low price of fossil fuels. Twenty years ago in Japan, more than two-hundred thousand solar water heaters were in use. Thirty years ago, Miami accounted for more than fifty thousand solar water heaters. Twenty years later, companies that had made Miami's fifty thousand heaters had either gone out of business or switched to manufacturing other products.

The declining cost of electricity and natural gas hurt the solar water heater industry. Like windmills used as an energy source on farms years ago, solar water heaters became popular in areas where other methods of heating water were either expensive or unavailable. But throughout this century, the area in which electricity and natural gas are available to consumers has increased rapidly, and the price of the energy (as a percentage of the homeowner's monthly bill) has steadily declined. As with gasoline or electrically powered water pumps compared to windmills, a point was reached where gas and electric water heaters were more convenient than solar water heaters, and a lot cheaper.

Now that the price of fossil fuels is rising, and will continue to rise for the foreseeable future, we should see some revitalization of the solar water heater industry. The price of sunlight has remained low—free is as low as you can get.

As will be shown in Chapter 10, solar water heating is already economically attractive for the individual house. There are two reasons for this: First, solar water heating generally requires simpler, cheaper equipment (and smaller collectors) than other domestic uses of solar energy; second, a family's requirements for hot water remain fairly steady throughout the year, so solar hot water equipment is used in an efficient manner and saves the family money all year long. Chapter 10 deals more fully with money savings, but the following figures give some perspective on the economic attractiveness of solar water heating.

Suppose everyone agreed to try to increase the total national supply of energy by one percent, to allow for increases in population and increases in *per capita* energy demand. And suppose it was decided to bring about this increase by concentrating entirely on increasing the amount of energy available for heating water.

There would be three reasonable ways of attaining this goal. First, we might agree to use solar water heaters in our homes. Second, we might import more liquefied natural gas (LNG). (Importing LNG would be necessary because of inadequate sources of natural gas within our country.) The third possibility would be to build more electric power plants for more electric water heating. This last idea would require that the country spend about fourteen billion dollars! The LNG approach would cost the country ten billion dollars. But the solar water heater option would require a national expenditure of only three billion dollars.

Given the principles behind domestic solar energy, as detailed

69

in Chapter 2, the design of solar water heaters is simplicity itself. A solar water heater is, usually, a water-based system with a flat plate collector, in which the heat storage medium (the water) is itself used to provide the hot water used in the house. Figure 9 shows a simplified design for one type of solarized water heater.

Note that in the type of heater shown in Figure 9, the storage tank is *above* the collector. This is a "passive" system, also called a "passive thermosyphoning" system. It takes advantage of the fact that hot water rises and cold water sinks. Water heated in the collector unit by the sun rises into the tank. Water inside the

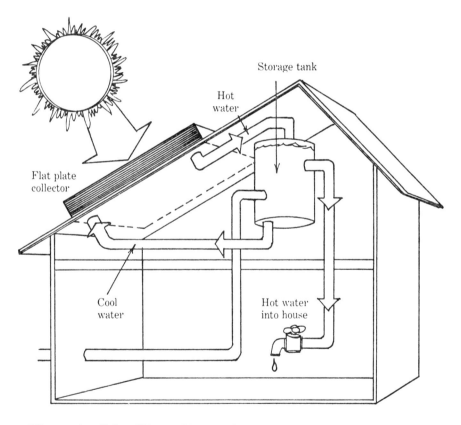

Figure 9—Solar Water Heater System

70

tank, as it cools, sinks through the bottom of the tank to a pipe leading back to the collector. The system is called passive because it uses the natural movement of hot and cold water ("thermal gradients"), rather than relying on a pump to move water. Since less water is needed overall than in a solar energy system that must heat a house, the passive system can do all the work required.

The drawback to this system is apparent in Figure 9. Not only must a roof be able to support the collector, but an attic must be able to support the storage tank filled with water as well. (In some passive designs, the tank is placed on the roof with the collector.) This weight leads to the problems of support discussed in Chapter 2. To avoid this, the solarized water heater is often an "active" system essentially the same as the space heating system shown in Figure 6, with the storage tank in the basement and a pump to keep water moving.

With such an arrangement, a family of four living in a fairly sunny climate would require a storage tank big enough to hold about eighty gallons of water and a flat plate collector with an area of about sixty square feet. (These numbers are based on a water temperature of 135°F for washing dishes and bathing, and a consumption rate of about twenty gallons per person per day. See Chapter 6 for a discussion of the impact of geographical location and local weather patterns on such domestic uses of solar energy.) An installation of this size should not be very expensive (about $1,000; see Chapter 10), and the savings in fuel costs should pay for the apparatus in under three years.

As with other applications of solar energy, reasonable size and cost for the apparatus can be obtained only by sacrificing total energy independence. A standby, or backup, fossil fuel water heater must be included in the design to take care of periods of extended cloudiness or unusually heavy use of hot water. Most of the time it should not be necessary to use this auxiliary heater, and, as discussed in Chapter 10, the homeowner with a solar water heater still ends up spending significantly less for fuel in the long run than the homeowner who depends entirely on electricity or natural gas.

71

To obtain water hotter than 135°F, the homeowner would have to increase the surface area of the collector. This would increase the price of the water heating system. But by greatly increasing the size of the collector and storage tank, a homeowner could reduce his dependence on an auxiliary heat source to almost zero. Still, for most parts of the country and for the hot water usage of most families, the "advantage" of hotter hot water or complete energy independence is just not worth the much higher price. (If you have a thermometer that goes high enough, such as one used in baking, you might try measuring the temperature of the water from the hot water tap in your kitchen. You'll probably find it's close to 135°F.) A fairly simple solar water heater, providing water at an adequate temperature and with an auxiliary heater (run by electricity or natural gas) built in, is highly practical and economically attractive.

The big drawback to the simple water-based system shown here is a general problem with water-based solar heating systems freezing. Corrosion and scale deposit remain a problem here, as in the water-based systems discussed in Chapter 2. But since one cannot have hot water without the water, scale deposit and corrosion are unavoidable. One cannot switch to an entirely air-based system to avoid the problems: The part of the system that provides water to the house must be water-based. Freezing—the most serious problem in terms of day-to-day operation—can be avoided.

The technique to avoid freezing is to divide the solar water heating system into two subsystems. One is the "heat-gathering subsystem," the other the "water-dispensing subsystem." The heat-gathering subsystem consists of the flat plate collector and two pipes connecting the collector to the storage tank. The water-dispensing subsystem is made up of the storage tank and pipes inside the house that provide hot water from the tank to residents. This system is sketched in Figure 10 by using shading to indicate piping and other hardware for the heat-gathering subsystem.

The importance of this separation into subsystems is this: Only the heat-gathering subsystem is ever exposed to below-freezing

72

temperatures, and only the water-dispensing subsystem need contain water. The solution to the problem of freezing is to separate the fluids in two subsystems, making the heat-gathering subsystem a closed cycle that may use antifreeze. Since the pipes carrying the hot working fluid from the collector pass through the water in the storage tank, they can be built in a corkscrew shape (one type of "heat exchanger") so the working fluid will pass most of its heat to water in the tank. (Heat radiating from the antifreeze into the water is depicted in the drawing by wiggly arrows.) As mentioned in Chapter 2, antifreeze entails problems, too—primarily cost. If the homeowner decides to use a completely water-based system, however, he must drain the water from the collector and exterior pipes whenever freezing temperatures are expected.

This matter also arises in the case of houses equipped with a solarized space heating system. If a homeowner also wants to have solarized hot water, he must take hot water needs into account when choosing a space heating system. Air-based systems are best overall for space heating, but he may feel a water-based system is the simplest for hot water, as it avoids heat exchangers. The homeowner could install two entirely separate systems, one air-based for space heating, and one water-based for hot water. Apart from the extra cost and the problems of fitting, pipes, storage tanks, and controls, this setup seems complicated and inefficient. A water-based system that provides space heat and hot water *seems* the simplest approach, but the homeowner runs into all the problems of water-based systems.

In the case of a system that provides heat and hot water, the problems of water-based systems take on an extra dimension. The usual version of such a system installed nowadays is essentially as described above—with two subsystems, one for heat gathering and one for water dispensing. In this case, the heat-gathering subsystem can include antifreeze, or it may use a fluid other than water. If that fluid is not air—in practice it is often water with antifreeze—then great care must be taken in the manufacture and installation of the heat exchanger. Whatever the design of the heat exchanger, the basic principle behind it is to

73

# At Home With Solar Energy

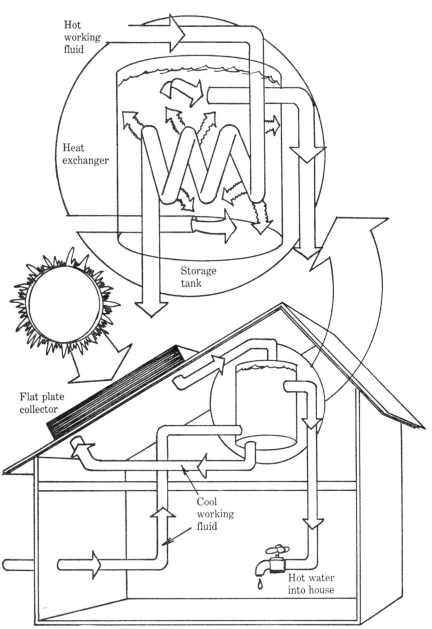

Hot working fluid

Heat exchanger

Storage tank

Flat plate collector

Cool working fluid

Hot water into house

Figure 10—Solar Water Heater System with Heat Exchanger

74

bring the two fluids into virtual contact, separated only by a wall or surface that transmits heat from one to the other. It is essential that there be no leakage of toxic materials, such as antifreeze, into the hot water used in the house; this could cause sickness or death.

The best way to avoid this danger, in a design in which heat exchangers must be used anyway, is to use air to collect heat and heat the house. *Via* the heat exchangers, this air can also heat water for use in the house.

## *Additional Reading*

*Basics of Solar Heating and Hot Water Systems.* A.I.A. Research Corporation, 1735 New York Ave., N.W., Washington, D.C. 20006. 1977.

Campbell, Stu. *Build Your Own Solar Water Heater.* Charlotte, Vt.: Garden Way Publishing, 1978. Designed for do-it-yourselfers, it provides background information and an introduction to the subject.

Clark, Wilson. *Energy for Survival.* New York: Doubleday, 1975. Pages 370-74.

Daniels, Farrington. *Direct Use of the Sun's Energy.* New York: Ballantine Books, 1975. Chapter 6.

Davey, E. T. *Solar Water Heating.* Environmental Action Reprint Service. (See Appendix.)

Kreider, Jan F. and Kreith, Frank. *Solar Heating and Cooling.* Washington, D.C.: Hemisphere Publishing Corporation, 1975. Pages 9-12.

Mahone, D. "Solar Hot Water Heating." *Solar Age* magazine, October, 1976

*Solar Hot Water and Your Home.* By the National Solar Heating and Cooling Information Center. (See Appendix.)

Stepler, Richard. "Solar Hot Water Heaters You Can Buy Now." *Popular Science*, June, 1976.

# 4
# HEATING
# YOUR HOME
# WITH
# SOLAR ENERGY

In general, the more complex the task a solar energy system must do, the more expensive the system becomes, and the less chance it has of competing economically with conventional systems that do the same thing.

The preceding chapter discussed using solar energy to heat water for the home, pointing out that a solar energy system designed for this purpose only is inexpensive to buy and have installed, is efficient and reliable, and is a good buy right now compared to more conventional water-heating systems. The next step up in complexity and usefulness is a solar energy system designed to heat a home—generally called "space heating." Unfortunately, such systems are more expensive than solar water heaters and, in some parts of the country, not yet a good buy compared to conventional methods used to heat homes. But as the cost of conventional fuels continues to increase and the cost of solar energy equipment decreases or holds steady, the percentage of American homeowners who would profit from choosing solar space heating over conventional means will increase dramatically.

The cost of fuel for space heating is a significant expense for the average family. We all buy energy in a variety of forms: gasoline for the family car; electricity for lights; electricity, natural gas, or fuel oil for space heating; and, for an increasing number of homes, electricity for air conditioning. For the average American family, 58 percent of the energy used in the home goes to space heating. This figure is a national average; the percentage is lower in southern Florida, and higher in northern Minnesota. The cost of this 58 percent is climbing steadily in almost all parts of the country, especially in the last few years. Yet the astonishing fact is that a house of average size receives, in a year, six times more energy in the form of sunlight shining on its roof than the family inside buys to heat the house!

The principle behind solar space heating is simple. The basis is a heat collection and storage system of the sort described in Chapter 2 (either air-based or water-based). Heat collected in water or rocks is distributed throughout the house by pipes, through which air or water heated in the storage bin is pumped. Figure 11 shows a simplified version of such a space heating system, in which an air-based system uses rocks for heat storage.

Generally, a solar space heating system will not heat a house entirely by itself: The most practical and economically attractive systems replace from 20 to 90 percent of the fuel used for heating houses that have not been solarized. Even a solarized house usually requires a standard, conventional space heating system as a backup. The homeowner will still have to buy from 10 to 80 percent of his energy from the local electric, natural gas, or fuel oil supplier. The exact percentage depends on a variety of factors—most importantly, geography.

Since sunlight provides the fuel for a solar energy space heating system, the more hours of sunlight the house receives in a day during cold weather, the better. This lessens the chance the house will have to rely on its backup system. It follows that solar space heating is less attractive the further north one lives, due to shorter winter days. In addition, houses in harsh northerly climates require more heat during winter. (More on this topic in Chapter 8.) Figure 12 shows the practicality of solar space heating for different parts of the country.

More localized factors are involved. The heat storage bin must be large enough to store heat for a period of time related to patterns of heat, cold, cloudiness, and sunshine in the area. The

77

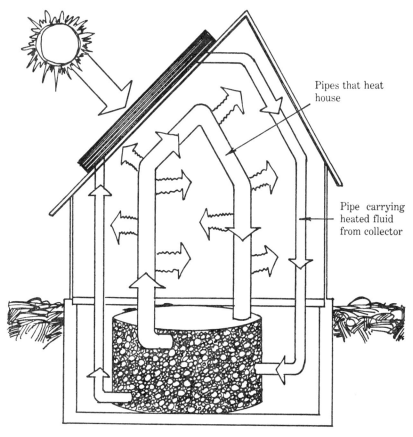

Pipes that heat house

Pipe carrying heated fluid from collector

Figure 11—Simple Solar Space Heating System

size of the collector and heat storage bin are partially determined by such local peculiarities as fog, pollution, and tall buildings casting shade on a house. These factors will be treated in greater detail in Chapter 8.

The central problem is the initial cost of a solar energy system—or, equivalently, how big it will be. This matter will be explained in more detail in Chapter 10; for now, we will present a broad overview.

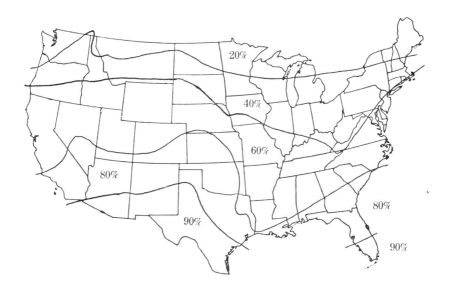

Figure 12—Estimated Percentage of Home Energy Needs a
Solar Energy System May Supply. (Note: This chart
should be used only as a general guide. Local conditions within the zones can vary greatly.) Adapted
from the journal *Heating and Ventilating*, Septem-
ber 1950, pp. 88–90.

Many consumer experts are distressed that the general public,
when planning major purchases, tends to concentrate on the price
of a product (its *initial cost*) rather than what the product will
really cost over its entire lifetime (its *life-cycle* cost). For example, the man who wants to buy a new car and is trying to choose
between two models—the Cheetah, let us say, and the Shark—
might decide to buy a Cheetah because, although both cars are
approximately the sort of vehicle he wants, the Cheetah is
cheaper. But suppose that the Shark, while somewhat more
expensive than the Cheetah, is also somewhat better designed
and made, so that the Shark will require fewer repairs, will

79

average better fuel economy, can be driven for longer before requiring regular maintenance, and, at the end, can be resold for a higher price. It may well be that all this will more than compensate for the higher initial price of the Shark, so that over the lifetime of the car, the purchaser would spend less in total if he bought the Shark rather than the Cheetah.

This total cost is the life-cycle cost of the car, and this approach (calculating the total cost of a product over its lifetime) is called *life-cycle costing*.

For a home in almost any part of the country, a solar space heating system could be designed to provide almost all of the home's heating needs. But this could be done only by making the system (especially the collector and heat storage bin) very large. The higher the percentage of solar-supplied energy one desires, the larger the system must be, and the more it will cost. Since a solar space heating system costs little to maintain, the life-cycle cost is roughly equal to the purchase and installation cost. Thus, squeezing those few extra percentage points out of sunlight (to reach 100 percent) greatly increases the life-cycle cost of a solar space heating system.

Due to mass production, widespread use, and long-standing public acceptance (and the hidden subsidies mentioned in Chapter 1), conventional space heating systems that provide all of a house's needs are normally built into new houses at a fairly reasonable cost—far less than the cost for a solar space heating system.

But conventional and solar space heating systems should be compared on the basis of life-cycle cost, rather than initial cost. For a conventional system, initial cost may not be extremely high, but fuel costs *are* high, and are rising. Because of this, in most parts of the country, solar space heating systems are now economically competitive, when life-cycle costs are compared. Chapter 10 will discuss how long it takes before the accumulated savings in fuel for a solar space heating system make up for the high purchase price.

*Additional Reading*

Daniels, George. *Solar Homes and Sun Heating.* New York: Harper & Row, 1976.

Lucas, Ted. *How to Build a Solar Heater.* Pasadena, Calif.: Ward Ritchie Press, 1975.

These are do-it-yourself books that provide background and an introduction to the subject.

# COOLING
# 5 YOUR HOME
# WITH
# SOLAR ENERGY

Strange as the idea may seem at first, the sun's heat can be used to cool your house.

An attractive feature of a solar cooling system is that the sunlight that heats the ordinary house beyond the point of comfort also provides the energy to keep the solarized house cool! The parts of the country where sunlight is most abundant and summer days the longest (southerly regions) are the areas where cooling is most needed and, simultaneously, where the life-cycle cost (see the preceding chapter) of a solar cooler would be lowest. The energy used by air conditioners averages four percent per home and is rising, as is the percentage of air conditioned homes. It takes as much energy to cool a house through a Texas summer as it does to heat a house through a Wisconsin winter.

Heating is generally needed more at night than during the day, and on cloudy days more than on sunny days. This means a solar space heating system must have a heat storage capacity sufficient to carry a house to the next sunny day. But as pointed out above, cooling is needed less if there is less sunshine. Therefore, solar cooling systems generally require smaller heat storage capacity than solar space heating systems. This translates into lower cost for the heat storage part of a solar cooling system.

Based on these considerations, it seems reasonable that solar cooling systems should be more economically attractive than solar space heating systems. The reason this is not so is that the technology required is not sufficiently developed. Interestingly, the method that will most likely be the one used when solar cooling does become practical (the absorption cycle, explained below) was used experimentally by Michael Faraday one hundred and fifty years ago. Equipment based on this principle (although it did not use solar energy) was manufactured in quantity fifty years ago. The widespread availability of cheap electricity made home-sized refrigeration equipment based on the vapor-compression cycle—which will also be explained—more readily available and more economical than absorption cycle equipment. As a result, the manufacture of home-sized absorption cycle equipment decreased and eventually stopped.

Unfortunately, it is not practical to convert vapor-compression cycle equipment to solar energy; most solar energy experts agree solar coolers require absorption cycle equipment. For solar coolers to compete economically with conventional air conditioning equipment, the absorption cycle equipment industry will have to recover its ability to produce home-sized equipment.

Only preliminary steps have been taken in this direction. Some solar energy experimenters, and a few small companies, have acquired designs and patents of defunct absorption cycle manufacturers, with a view toward modifying the equipment and adapting it to solar energy. At least one of the older manufacturers of absorption cycle coolers has resumed production of a model that interests solar energy experimenters.

Despite all this, there is no solar cooler this book can recommend to the homeowner. This chapter is included because it is conceivable that solar coolers *will* be available commercially within five to ten years. If that happens, they will be a very attractive buy. The consumer who understands the principles behind the available equipment in the future will be in a good position to make the wisest possible purchase.

Refrigerators and air conditioners now in home use are based on the "vapor-compression cycle." The vapor-compression cycle relies on the fact that a substance absorbs heat when it vaporizes and releases heat when it condenses (changes from a vapor to a liquid). The idea of the vapor-compression cycle is to vaporize a liquid (the "refrigerant") within the enclosure to be cooled (a refrigerator or an air conditioner). The vapor, which has absorbed heat, is transported outside the enclosure, and finally condensed back into a liquid, still outside the enclosure. Thus the heat carried by the vapor is released to the outside. The final step—the condensation of the refrigerant back into a liquid—is called "regeneration." With the cycle completed, the liquid refrigerant can now be pumped back into the air conditioner or refrigerator so the process can be repeated. Many substances make adequate refrigerants; the most widely used are chemical compounds known as fluorinated hydrocarbons, widely known under the trade name "Freon."

Figure 13 shows a simplified picture of the technology used in the vapor-compression cycle. Note that the refrigerant is condensed with a "compressor" (hence the name of the cycle), and

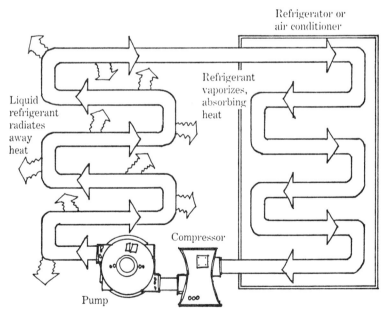

Figure 13—Simplified Vapor-Compression Cycle Cooling System

84

that a pump is necessary. In the case of an air conditioner, a fan is also needed, to blow cold air into a room. This is where solar energy could come into play. Stored heat of the sun could be used to power a "heat engine" (such devices exist), which in turn could run the compressor and pump. The low efficiency of such systems that have been built has made them impractical; raising the efficiency significantly would require much higher temperatures than a reasonably priced solar energy system with flat plate collector could deliver. All in all, the solar energy-operated heat engine is not a promising technology for home use, though it might prove useful some day to industry. This forces us to eliminate the vapor-compression cycle from consideration as the basis for solar coolers.

The other method of cooling is the "absorption cycle," sometimes called the "absorption-desorption cycle." This cycle is also based on the principle of using a refrigerant that absorbs heat by evaporating, then releases the heat elsewhere by returning to a liquid. But this is done in a more complicated way than in the vapor-compression cycle, as Figure 14 illustrates.

The unique feature of the absorption cycle is that the refrigerant, while still a vapor, returns to liquid form not by condensation in a compressor, but rather by absorption into another substance, a liquid called the "absorbent." The device where this takes place is shown as the "absorber" in Figure 14. This process requires no energy from outside, because the refrigerant and absorbent have been chosen so that the latter will absorb the former on exposure, due to the properties of the chemicals. This absorption also reduces pressure in the coils labeled "evaporating refrigerant," thus encouraging the refrigerant, which enters the coils at the top as a liquid, to evaporate and absorb heat.

The heat absorbed by the evaporating refrigerant is radiated away by the liquid—the refrigerant-absorbent solution. In experimental solar coolers, this requires fairly complex hardware, including a large cooling tower. The cooled liquid solution is pumped to a regenerator, where the refrigerant is once again separated from the absorbent so the cycle can be repeated.

The chemicals have been chosen so the refrigerant has a much

At Home With Solar Energy

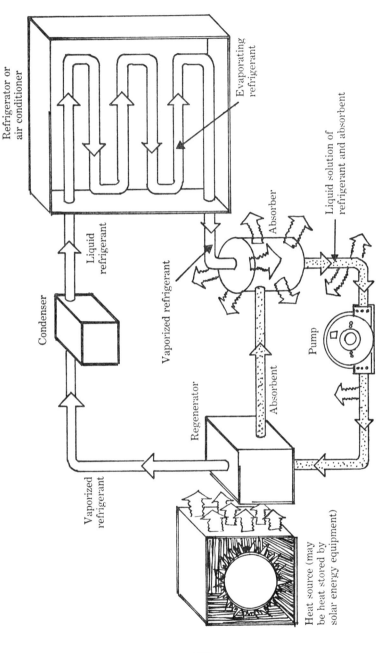

Figure 14—Simplified Absorption Cycle Cooling System

lower boiling point than the absorbent. Therefore, all that is necessary for regeneration is to heat the solution until the refrigerant boils and evaporates, leaving the absorbent, which is still well below its own boiling point. In commercial absorption coolers, the heat required at this step is usually provided by burning kerosene or natural gas. Here solar energy enters the picture, for this heat can be provided by a flat plate collector and a heat storage bin.

The absorbent returns to the absorber tank to repeat its part of the cycle. Meanwhile the refrigerant, which was evaporated out of the solution in the regenerator, moves up the pipe to the condenser. The condenser is needed because the refrigerant, which is still a vapor, must be a liquid to begin its cycle again when it enters the coils to evaporate and absorb heat. Since the refrigerant cools the space within the large rectangle in Figure 14 (the refrigerator or air conditioner) by absorbing heat and evaporating, it must be in liquid form when it enters the rectangle.

Because of the nature of the refrigerants used in absorption cycle coolers, the condenser can be a much simpler device than the compressor used in the vapor-compression cycle. It need not be a big energy-user. In absorption cycle coolers where the refrigerant is ammonia and the absorbent is water, it is possible to have a condenser that consists simply of water at room temperature through which the pipe carrying vaporized ammonia passes. (The other popular combination is to use water as the refrigerant, with lithium bromide as the absorbent.)

Since the absorption cooler does not require a compressor, much energy is saved in comparison with vapor-compression cycle equipment. It is also possible to design an absorption cycle cooler that has no pump; instead, it would use the tendency of hot liquids to rise and cold liquids to fall. Such a design would require no outside energy except the heat for regenerating the refrigerant—and that, as pointed out above, could be provided by a solar energy device.

Great difficulties stand in the way of practical solar absorption coolers. Ammonia is toxic. With a water/lithium bromide cooler, crystallization can occur in the regenerator. In certain designs, the regenerator requires a lot of heat, which means a large solar collector area that is costly to install.

Related to the matter of cooling a house is the problem of dehumidifying it. In certain climates the problem is crucial because of the high humidity of the outside air. As temperatures drop, the water-carrying capacity of air also drops. If the air holds a great deal of water, close to its capacity, we say humidity is high. If the temperature of air drops, as it does when brought into an air conditioned house, water represents a greater percentage of the air's water-carrying capacity; humidity has increased. This makes the air less comfortable, offsetting the cooling effect of the air conditioner. In very humid climates, the outside humidity may already be close to 100 percent, so lowering the air's temperature and water-carrying capacity can push the air's (relative) humidity *over* 100 percent. This results in water condensing on surfaces inside the house, which can lead to all types of damage, especially to paint and furniture. If an air conditioner is solarized and the refrigerant is water, even the smallest leak in the air conditioner's piping increases the problem. Whether problems of this sort will delay the commercialization of solarized air conditioners remains to be seen.

If and when solar cooling becomes practical for the individual home, the solar energy system that will be most attractive will be one that combines the applications discussed above: water heating, space heating, and home cooling. Such a system would be used to the maximum throughout the year, recovering in a relatively few years in fuel savings the cost of purchase and installation. (More on this in Chapter 10.)

Practical solar cooling might some day have a profound and positive effect on world affairs. In most developing countries, heat and sunlight are abundant, while energy is scarce and expensive. Factories are intolerably hot, severely reducing workers' productivity. Important foods cannot even be used, because they spoil rapidly. Of crops that are raised, as much as one-fourth may be lost to spoilage. These countries cannot afford fuel to run conventional cooling equipment—but their climates are ideal for solar coolers. Who knows how many political problems of the Third World are really caused by a combination of poverty, hunger, and heat? Perhaps it is not unrealistic to hope that practical solar cooling may be one key to world peace!

# 6 ENERGY-EFFICIENT HOME DESIGN

For most of us, the word *house* conjures up a picture of a box-like building, with a roof that looks rather like the two flaps that form the cover of the box. This box is an accurate picture of the average modern American home. Add to this picture inadequate insulation, windows whose size and direction of view bear little or no relationship to daily and annual changes in sunlight, and a landscape denuded of trees by the original housing developer, and it becomes clear the typical modern house is an enormous waster of energy.

Many architects around the country specialize in designing houses that use the heating and cooling facilities provided by nature. Even if you have no intention of hiring an architect to design a house for you, the general discussion of design criteria in this chapter should guide you on what to look for the next time you want to buy a house. Even tract houses are not all alike (yet!), and the factors that make one house a more economical user of power company energy than another, and also a better user of the energy provided by nature, should figure into a purchase decision as strongly as the building's exterior beauty or the closeness of schools, shopping centers, and places of work. The portion of an average family's income gobbled up by the purchase of energy for a house is large, and going up so quickly that it is a major part of the cost of owning a house. Any potential savings in this area should not be ignored.

Even without the question of solarizing a house—including a solar water heater or a solar space heater—the design of a house, the materials used in its construction, its site, its orientation with respect to compass directions, and the nature of the surrounding landscape can have an enormous effect on how expensive the house is to own, and how comfortable it is to live in.

Primitive man knew this. He learned to avoid the sun in hot climates, and to minimize heat loss from his home in cold places. Indians of the Gulf Coast area and natives of the South Seas both favored light-weight construction, avoiding materials that would absorb heat during the day and radiate it back into the house during the night. Often they lived in buildings that were all roof, with little or no walls beyond the necessary supports. This provided shade during the day and allowed cooling breezes to blow through the house. At the other climatic extreme, Eskimos learned to build well-insulated houses, using a design that reduces heat loss to a minimum. The basic design of the igloo (the Eskimo word for *house*) used in winter was a dome, with much of the living space below ground level. The dome was covered with sod for insulation, and its entrance was a covered passageway, often with a dip in it to interrupt heat flow. (The ice or snow house we usually call an igloo was only a temporary dwelling.)

The importance of orientation—the angle of the house with respect to the sun—has long been recognized. The Romans, when building in cooler climates, strove for southern exposures for the fronts of buildings, to take maximum advantage of the warmth of the sun, which is low in the south during winter. New England colonists put the kitchen on the north side of a house, so that the stove, which was kept burning constantly as a heat source, would help warm that side of the house. (The north side of a house was always coldest, because of the prevailing north wind during winter, and the lack of sunlight on the north side of any building in our part of the northern hemisphere.) The principles discovered and used by these peoples throughout history are still valid.

91

Incorporating them in the design of our houses will make the resulting buildings more comfortable and economical. But these principles are all too often ignored.

Why did we stop building sensible, economical, and energy-efficient houses? We discovered cheap energy, mass production, and what might be called mass construction. The emphasis turned to putting up many houses, as quickly as possible, in order to capitalize on a rapidly expanding market. This dictated standardized designs that were determined more by mass construction techniques than local climates. Insulation was decreased year by year to keep costs in line. No one worried much about energy loss, because the increasing abundance of cheap energy (primarily electricity and natural gas) meant central heating could keep the house warm. It was not as obvious that careful, individualized design, construction, and insulation could have made houses more comfortable during summer, too, by reducing the absorption of heat from the sun and the inflow of heat from outside air—but once air conditioners became commercially practical, even this no longer mattered much. Only now, with our monthly bills for oil, natural gas, and electricity shooting up relentlessly, and with politicians uttering solemn warnings about the energy crisis day after day, are we becoming aware of the energy inefficiency inherent in standard home designs.

In practice, modern house design simply cannot use all the principles discovered by older cultures throughout history. For one thing, most Americans live in areas where there are distinct seasons, so a house must withstand both summer heat and winter cold. Primitives and the very wealthy can resolve this dilemma by migrating twice a year, or by having different homes for summer and winter; neither solution is practical for most of us. Most people would also prefer that their houses not look strange on the outside. Today's house designer also has to take into account the ready availability of standard materials and construction techniques; special materials or techniques inevitably drive up the cost of a house. (Chapter 12 gives examples of unusual, energy efficient, solarized houses built by solar energy experimenters who did not feel constrained by conventional ideas on a house's appearance.)

If you plan to build a house rather than buy an existing one, you are generally at an advantage. Some people, such as those discussed in Chapter 12, choose to design and build their own highly energy efficient house. For most people, however, the sensible alternative is to hire an architect. It is imperative that they find an architect who is knowledgeable (and preferably experienced) in the area of energy efficiency in building design, and who knows how to use sunlight and landscaping to an advantage. This chapter will give general rules for house design, and Chapter 8 will discuss geographic factors that must be taken into account; a good architect will be able to use all these facts to design for specific local conditions of weather and terrain.

For most of the population of the United States, the main aim in house design must be heat gain and retention for more than half the year. The house itself should act as much like a solar heating system as possible, gaining heat from sunlight during the day, and emitting heat to the interior of the house during night. Like the solar heating systems discussed in Chapters 2 and 4, the house itself must be of the proper shape and orientation to collect heat, must be heat-tight and adequately insulated to avoid losing heat, and must be constructed of the proper materials to store heat and release it into the house at night.

To act like a collector, the house should be rectangular in shape, rather than square. The long axis of the rectangle should run east-west; one of the two longer outside walls should face south (see Figure 15). A good rule of thumb is that the longer sides of this rectangle should be about twice as long as the shorter sides. Heat absorption will be increased if the south-facing wall is painted a dark color. To help make the house a good solar collector, windows should be concentrated as much as possible in the south wall. A two-story house designed on these principles will be an even better collector of solar heat than a one-story house, because of greater surface area exposed to the sun.

Like a good collector system, a house must not lose to the

outside air the heat it gains from the sun. The most important factor in this respect is insulation. This includes the insulating effect of walls, floors, and ceilings, the materials they are made of, and the insulating materials added to them.

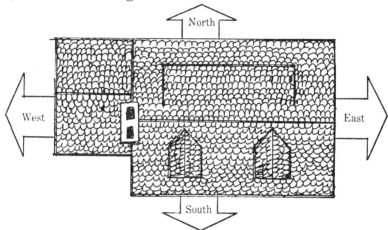

Figure 15—Best House Shape and Orientation for Solar Energy Use

A house should be air tight, for insulation will do little good if heat leaks out through gaps and cracks around doors and windows. This is not a matter of architectural design so much as how well the architect's design is executed—how well the house is put together.

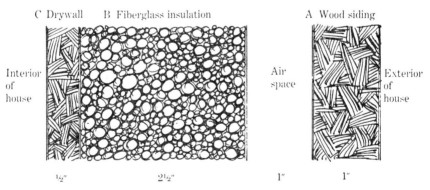

Figure 16—A Hypothetical Exterior Wall

Two hundred years ago, men of science talked of heat and electricity as fluids that "flowed." We now know electricity is a rather more complicated phenomenon. But we still talk of "heat flow," for it's a useful concept. Heat tends to flow from places where there is more of it to places where there is less: Nature's tendency is to equalize heat distribution. Thus, heat tends to flow out of a house during winter. Assuming a house is air tight, most of this flow occurs through walls and the roof. Insulation keeps that heat flow down to an acceptable level. We say "acceptable" level rather than "zero," because to try to reach zero heat flow would require an enormous expense—far more than the comfort and decreased heating bills would justify. (It would be impossible to actually attain zero heat flow.) The level of heat flow—heat loss—that is acceptable depends on the cost of insulation material compared to the cost of fuel. It also depends on the climate, since the amount of heat flowing out of a house depends partly upon the difference in temperature between inside and outside air; the greater the difference, the greater the heat flow. A house in a cold climate requires more insulation than one in a mild climate, if the heat loss is to be kept to the same level in both. (See Chapter 9 for more details.) The heat loss through a particular wall of a house also depends on winds that can be expected to blow on it. This in turn depends on local climate and terrain. Insulation requirements for a wall are determined partly by the local climate and the shape of the land around the house.

(You should be careful not to spend money insulating the wrong parts of your house. Some cities have companies that will, for a reasonable fee, take an infrared photograph of a house to determine where the largest heat loss occurs.)

Insulation means more than special insulating materials inserted into walls and placed on the attic floor. Such insulation is important, but the material of which the house is constructed also plays a role in cutting down heat flow. The insulating ability of insulation and construction materials is measured as the *R-factor* ("resistance factor"). You will also see this referred to as "R-value." The higher the R-factor of a material, the better it insulates or resists the flow of heat through it. One-inch-thick softwood

95

siding has an R-factor of 1.25, while hardwood siding of the same thickness has an R-factor of .91, and is therefore a less effective insulator. Increasing the thickness of a material cuts down on heat flow and increases the R-factor. The difference in insulating ability among various materials can be surprising. A one-eighth-inch-thick piece of glass (R-factor .89) insulates as well as eight inches of concrete (R-factor .88). R-factors tables can be found, along with much more solar data, in a handbook published by ASHRAE—the American Society of Heating, Air-conditioning, and Refrigerating Engineers (see list at the end of this chapter).

These R-factors are added to obtain the R-factor of a combination of materials. For example, consider the sketch of the exterior wall shown in Figure 16, where A is wood siding on the outside of the wall, one inch thick, R-factor .91; B is fiberglass insulation, 2½ inches thick, R-factor 7.8; and C is the drywall on the inside surface of the wall, one-half-inch thick, R-factor .45. To obtain the insulating power, or R-factor, of this wall, add the above numbers. But this ignores the insulating effect of air. Note that there is a one-inch space between A and B—the siding and the fiberglass insulation. This air-space has an R-factor of .9, which must be included in this calculation. Surprisingly, there is also an effect from the layer of air *against* the exterior of the wall, which has an R-factor of about .15, and from the still air inside the house—an R-factor of about .7. Adding these R-factors—outside air, siding, air space within the wall, insulation, drywall, inside air—gives a total of 10.91 for the entire wall. The same sort of calculation could be performed for ceilings. Whether the resulting R-factor is high enough depends on local conditions; local governments and power companies can usually recommend minimum R-factors for walls and ceilings in their areas.

Such calculations influence an architect's design of an energy-efficient house. R-factors influence the architect's choice of materials, dimensions, and even the design of the attic, since this has a bearing on the R-factor of the air-space above the ceiling.

The house should hold heat during the day and return it to the interior at night. The less heat allowed to escape through walls and windows, the warmer the house will be at night. Construction materials exist that will absorb heat and retain it, thus acting as heat storage. The use of such materials throughout the house can result in a home where inside air stays at a nearly constant temperature, with only a minimum of heat added by a furnace, or solar space heater. The air inside a cave or a deep hole in the ground is not greatly affected by the temperature of outside air; there is an advantage in making a house kind of an extension of the ground. Unfortunately, fashion is a villain here. Designing for good heat storage requires using lots of concrete, little glass, and very thick walls—and this applies to interior as well as exterior walls. The light, airy, glass-covered look popular today discourages such massive-looking buildings.

If you have protested all along that you live in a warm climate, and your problem is not heating your house but cooling it, take heart. The design criteria mentioned above that make the house good at retaining heat and giving it back to the interior at night also keep the house cool in warmer climates. It was said about heat earlier that it flows from warmer to cooler places. This applies to heat flowing out of a house in cold weather, *as well as* heat flowing into a house when outside air is warmer than inside air. Insulation and weatherstripping help keep a house cooler during warm days, just as they help keep heat in when the weather is cold. The sort of massive construction discussed above stores cool as well as heat. Massive construction actually enables the walls of a house to absorb heat from inside air; the effect is the same as if the walls could store coolness. A massively designed house doesn't warm up quickly during hot weather.

Making a house a good *collector* of solar energy is a more difficult matter. If cooling the house is the primary concern, then an architect essentially has to reverse all of the advice in this area. Deciding which is more important for a given part of the country—heating or cooling—is vital. This issue will be treated in detail in Chapter 8.

Summer heat is a problem in much of the country. Here is one clever method of preventing south-facing windows from picking up heat during summer. Simply plant trees in front of the windows! Not evergreen trees, but deciduous trees—those that lose their leaves during autumn. A good shade tree will block sunlight during the summer, and will lose its leaves to let in sunlight (solar heat) during winter. Another idea is to place awnings over windows. The sun is higher in the sky during summer than winter. As Figure 17 shows, an awning placed over a window at the proper angle will admit sunlight during winter but will shade the window during summer. This serves the same function as a deciduous tree, but of course awnings don't take years to grow!

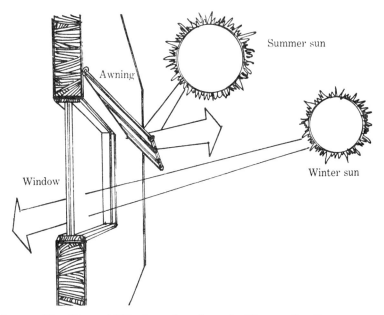

Figure 17—Use of Window Awnings in Home Cooling

An idea that deserves mention is using windbreaks to protect the house—especially its north side. A windbreak may be a stand of trees, although this involves waiting years until the desired effect is achieved. Another method is to build hills into the landscaping. The hills need not be very large; small hills can do the trick, if local prevailing winds are properly measured beforehand and the hills are appropriately placed and shaped. Figure 18 shows how to divert the troublesome north wind with a hill. The shape of the house is important in this respect, as it contributes to channeling the winds in a favorable way. A clever architect will take such matters into account in his house designs.

Figure 18—Using a Hill to Break the Chilling Effect of the North Wind

Everything discussed in this chapter so far involves using nature's resources to fullest advantage. Designing houses so they can have solar energy machinery included from the beginning or added later with relative ease, imposes extra constraints on an architect.

If solar collectors are to be mounted on a house's roof, the roof should have the proper south-facing tilt. There should be enough roof area facing south at the correct angle so collectors may be mounted on it easily. If this is not the case, a superstructure will have to be added, and this may mean a problem with local building codes. (Not to mention the extra cost.) In any case, there is also the problem of the weight of the collectors. This can be signifi-cant, especially with a water-based system. So an architect must be sure to design roof supports to withstand this extra weight. The architect must take the collector, with its area, tilt, and weight, into account; he must also consider the hardware described in Chapters 2 through 4. Solar energy equipment requires room, and this must be designed into the house. If the storage system (a tank of water or rocks) is to be placed in the basement, room must be provided. Solar energy means extensive piping, of a different sort than conventional heating systems, and the architect must provide for this. As mentioned earlier, solarized houses still need backup conventional heating systems, so the architect must allow room for the solar system as well as a conventional system. All this, and yet the architect must still come up with a design that pleases the eye and the pocketbook!

It is important that the consumer who is buying an existing home, rather than having one built for him, should look for a house that meets the above criteria. It is too much to hope that a house built by a tract developer will have been constructed with the above principles in mind. But the more a house reflects these design principles, the better—and the cheaper—it will be to operate, and the more comfortable it will be. Should an owner decide to add solar energy to his house at a future date, he may be faced with great expense and endless trouble if none of the above design principles has been incorporated into his house.

*Additional Reading*

Anderson, Bruce. *The Solar Home Book*. Harrisville, N.H.: Cheshire Books, 1976. Excellent. Essential if you want to build the whole house yourself, but an overabundance of detail if you're going to buy an existing house.

*ASHRAE Handbook of Fundamentals*. New York: American Society of Heating, Refrigerating, and Air Conditioning Engineers, 1974. A solar energy bible; all you could ever want to know about R-factors—and more than you probably want to know about lots of other factors.

Crowther, Richard L. *Sun, Wind, Earth*. Denver: Solar Group, Architects, 1977. Interesting background information on topics discussed in this chapter but written more for architects than consumers. Make sure your architect reads it!

Kreider, Jan F. and Kreith, Frank. *Solar Heating and Cooling.* Washington, D.C.: Scripta Book Company, 1975. Same comments apply as for *Sun, Wind, Earth.*

Stein, Richard G. *Architecture and Energy.* New York: Anchor Books/Doubleday, 1978. Same as for *Sun, Wind, Earth.*

Wright, David. *Natural Solar Architecture: A Passive Primer.* New York: Van Nostrand, Reinhold Co., 1978. Similar comments to *Sun, Wind, Earth.*

# ADDING SOLAR ENERGY TO THE EXISTING HOUSE

Including a solar energy system in your new house as the house is being built for you is fine—if you can afford an architect, an original design, and the construction costs. But if you're like most people, you'll want to know about *retrofitting*, or adding solar energy equipment to the house you live in or want to buy. The feasibility of retrofitting depends heavily on the nature of an individual house, so unfortunately no general answer can be given as to whether retrofitting is right for your home. To make such a decision you need a solar appraisal of your home by a competent engineering firm. (Such appraisals will be treated in Chapter 10.)

When you ask whether retrofitting is worth while, you are really asking about economics. Here the question is not, "Is it technically feasible to retrofit my home?" but, "Is it worth the expense, given some reasonable guess at the cost?"

If you're hunting for a house to which you want to add solar equipment, you should take into account the design criteria discussed in the preceding chapter. The degree to which an existing house matches these criteria should be a factor in your decision whether to buy the house.

There is no simple answer to the issue of retrofitting. There are two answers—"yes" and "no"—and there are arguments to support both sides. This and subsequent chapters will summarize the two schools of thought and present calculations you can perform that should help in any decision you make. Every house is different, as is every geographical location. The right decision on retrofitting for one person might well be the wrong one for another.

One school of thought on the issue argues against retrofitting, because of the changes in the house's structure such equipment might require. Most houses were not designed to some day accomodate solar energy equipment, and would require structural changes because of the angle of the roof's tilt and the roof area available for collector panels. Something would probably also have to be done to let the house bear the great added weight of collector panels and piping. Most or all of the space in the basement would be needed for a heat storage tank. This restructuring means a lot of money, in addition to the actual cost of the solar energy equipment itself. One estimate is that it can cost from 50 to 100 percent more to retrofit than to add solar energy equipment to a house not yet built. Perhaps most frustrating of all, financing may be almost impossible to find for retrofitting. In many parts of the country it's now hard to find bank money for a new house designed to be solarized; trying to persuade these institutions to finance retrofitting is all but hopeless.

Even if retrofitting is accomplished in the face of obstacles, the result is a solar system that operates much less efficiently than solar energy equipment built into a new house. This means you would save less conventional fuel than you might expect, and that the payback period—the time before money saved on conventional fuel pays for the solar energy equipment—is much longer than you might want. Add the higher initial cost of retrofitting (compared to solarizing the design of a new house), and you are probably ready to ask, "Why bother?" The only way to increase the efficiency of a retrofit system is to add a lot of insulation and weatherstripping to the house. This itself represents an expense that must be covered in a reasonable amount of time by money saved on fuel.

"Stuff and nonsense," the other school of thought on retrofitting replies. Any poorly designed and/or insulated house wastes energy, solarizing aside. So this school feels you might as well go ahead and install solar energy equipment and "waste" free sunlight, rather than waste fuel you have to pay for. The way fuel prices keep shooting up, the payback period might not be as long as you might expect. Better to pay for structural work and solar energy equipment than pay high fuel costs in the future, this school argues. Insulation and weatherstripping can be added bit by bit, whereas solarizing, practically speaking, must be done at once.

Some solar energy experts think financing may not be as serious a matter as it once was. In many parts of the country, lending institutions are at last becoming educated on solarization: Solar energy equipment no longer seems to them an expensive and frivolous luxury, and the institutions are becoming somewhat more willing to pass loans for new houses with solar equipment or loans for retrofitting an existing house. The federal government will soon underwrite such loans, grant low-interest loans directly to the homeowner, or devise some sort of tax break for homeowners who retrofit. At the time of this writing, no legislation to enable government to enter the solarization loan field has made it through Congress, but a number of senators and representatives are making brave noises. With increasing public eagerness for such legislation, and with increasing numbers of votes to be gained at reelection time by sponsors of such laws, one can hope something will happen soon. If and when it does, lending institutions, knowing they no longer bear all the risk for this "exotic" new energy source, should become far more willing to offer loans for retrofitting.

As is so often the case in disagreements, the two schools of thought on the question of retrofitting seem to have made up their minds long ago, based in some cases on economic or philosophical biases. Which of these points of view appeals to you is a matter of taste. This book favors retrofitting.

If a roof's angle is wrong but its surface area is large, extra solar panels can be added to a collector. This will enable the system to collect enough solar heat, even though the angle may not be optimum. This increases the cost of the equipment, but the

104

increase may well be less than the cost of rebuilding a roof to attain the proper angle. The cost of solar energy equipment should hold steady or even decrease over the next few years. At any rate, you must consider the actual costs that apply in your case before making a decision. A way out of the difficulty for homeowners whose roofs are not set at the proper angle is to place the collector in their yard. This is also an appealing alternative for houses with roofs having a surface area too small for collector systems, and for houses that cannot support the weight of a rooftop collector system.

Such freestanding systems—which were discussed in Chapter 2—are not without drawbacks. They take up a fair amount of yard space. (On the other hand, they also eliminate that much lawn that would otherwise need mowing!) Placing the collector at ground level may add the problem of keeping it out of shade, whether from trees, shrubs, or other buildings. Some homeowners may fear that the sight of a collector in the yard will lower the resale value of a house. (An enlightened buyer would be delighted to find the hard work of solarizing the house done for him.) And there is, unfortunately, the problem of vandalism: The ground-level collector is usually more vulnerable than one on a roof. As mentioned in Chapter 2, should you decide to have a collector at ground level, you might also want to have your storage system outside—perhaps underground, beneath the collector. This involves a fair amount of earth-moving, which costs more money, but it avoids using basement space or having space excavated *under* the basement for a heat storage tank. More piping would also be required for the sort of freestanding system discussed here.

# GEOGRAPHY: WHERE YOU LIVE MAKES A DIFFERENCE

8

Because solar energy systems depend on the sun to function, the size and design of a particular collector system depends on how much sunlight is available at a given house's location. Actually, the amount of sunlight a homeowner can expect to shine on his house in a day varies greatly from one part of the country to another. This means collector and storage system will have to be larger in some areas than in others; it also means solarizing a house will cost more in some places than others. The fewer hours of sunlight a house receives, the less a solar energy system will be able to bear the load of heating. This means more conventional energy will have to be used, extending the payback time for the solar energy system. In some parts of the country, solarizing one's house is not economically practical at present. Whether it will become practical in those areas depends on a number of developments: What will happen to the price of conventional fuels in those areas; what will happen to the prices of solar energy equipment; and what will Congress do in the area of tax refunds for solar energy purchases or federal underwriting or loans. Technological breakthroughs in the design and manufacture of solar energy equipment might bring the price of such hardware down dramatically while raising its efficiency, but the picture is not encouraging for the northernmost parts of the United States.

Table 2. Hours of Sunlight by Latitude

| Latitude (Degrees) | City | Maximum Hours and Minutes (June 21) | Minimum Hours and Minutes (December 22) |
|---|---|---|---|
| 27½ | Tampa | 13h, 50m | 10h, 25m |
| 30 | New Orleans | 14h, 5m | 10h, 15m |
| 32½ | Dallas | 14h, 15m | 10h, 0m |
| 35 | Albuquerque | 14h, 30m | 9h, 50m |
| 37½ | San Francisco | 14h, 45m | 9h, 35m |
| 40 | Philadelphia | 15h, 0m | 9h, 20m |
| 42½ | Milwaukee | 15h, 15m | 9h, 0m |
| 45 | Minneapolis | 15h, 35m | 8h, 45m |
| 47½ | Seattle | 16h, 0m | 8h, 25m |

Adapted from *Travelling Weatherwise in the U.S.A.*, by Edward Powers and James Witt. © 1973 by Edward Powers and James Witt. Used by permission of Dodd, Mead & Company.

Table 2 shows the range of hours (and minutes) of sunshine for various latitudes, from the Gulf Coast to the Canadian border, with a value given for every 2½ degree change in latitude. The cities listed are at or near the latitude given. The amount of sunshine is shown for each latitude for June 21 (the longest day of the year) and for December 22 (the shortest). At first glance, one might conclude from the table that one is better off living further north, at least for the purpose of maximizing hours of sunlight, since the length of day during summer is much greater than in southern cities. But this is not all there is to the matter. At the North Pole the sun never sets during summer, meaning there are twenty-four hours of sunlight every day—yet the North Pole is not noted for a warm climate. The last column in Table 2 shows the other factor we must consider: The further south one lives, the less the seasonal variation in the length of day. In Tampa the longest day is about one-third again as long as the shortest day; in

107

Seattle the longest day is about *twice* as long as the shortest day. Of course the length of day during winter matters most to the owner of a solarized house.

Table 2 shows how sunlight varies with latitude. Specific figures can usually be obtained to show the average hours of sunlight during each month for a particular city. In general, these figures vary with latitude in the way shown in Table 2. But for those interested in using solar energy equipment another factor must be considered. Different parts of the country have very different climates, so the amount of sunlight one might expect in a given city based on the city's latitude may be far *more* than the city will probably receive. Solar energy experts usually talk in terms of average hours of *useful* sunlight, or how much useable sunlight a solar collector in a given city can reasonably expect.

For a rough idea of what this means, consult Table 3. It shows the hours of sunlight one can expect on an average summer or winter day and in an average year. The figures cannot be precise, but they provide a basis for comparing different parts of the country.

### Table 3. Hours of Sunshine in the United Sates

Average Daily Hours of Sunshine

|  | Summer*<br>(Daily) | Winter**<br>(Daily) | Annual |
|---|---|---|---|
| Alabama | | | |
| Birmingham | 9.0 | 4.7 | 2662 |
| Mobile | 8.7 | 5.1 | 2708 |
| Montgomery | 9.7 | 5.4 | 2894 |
| Arizona | | | |
| Phoenix | 12.3 | 8.1 | 3832 |
| Prescott | 11.1 | 7.6 | 3549 |
| Tuscon | 11.4 | 8.6 | 3829 |
| Yuma | 13.1 | 8.7 | 4077 |
| Arkansas | | | |
| Fort Smith | 10.1 | 5.0 | 2747 |
| Little Rock | 10.4 | 4.9 | 2840 |
| California | | | |
| Eureka | 7.7 | 4.1 | 2198 |

*Average daily hours of sunshine during June, July, and August.
**Average daily hours of sunshine during December, January, and February.

108

# Geography: Where You Live Makes a Difference

|  | Summer (Daily) | Winter (Daily) | Annual |
|---|---|---|---|
| Fresno | 13.7 | 5.4 | 3632 |
| Los Angeles | 10.7 | 7.3 | 3284 |
| Red Bluff | 13.5 | 5.5 | 3468 |
| Sacramento | 13.6 | 4.7 | 3422 |
| San Diego | 8.9 | 7.2 | 2958 |
| San Francisco | 9.8 | 5.6 | 2959 |
| Colorado |  |  |  |
| Denver | 10.1 | 6.7 | 3033 |
| Grand Junction | 11.0 | 5.8 | 3095 |
| Pueblo | 10.9 | 7.2 | 3270 |
| Connecticut |  |  |  |
| Hartford | 9.3 | 4.9 | 2541 |
| New Haven | 9.6 | 5.4 | 2704 |
| Distr. of Columbia |  |  |  |
| Washington | 9.2 | 4.8 | 2576 |
| Florida |  |  |  |
| Apalachicola | 9.0 | 6.2 | 2941 |
| Jacksonville | 8.3 | 6.1 | 2713 |
| Key West | 8.9 | 7.7 | 3098 |
| Lakeland | 8.3 | 6.5 | 2732 |
| Miami | 8.5 | 7.3 | 2903 |
| Pensacola | 9.4 | 5.8 | 2918 |
| Tampa | 8.5 | 7.2 | 3001 |
| Georgia |  |  |  |
| Atlanta | 9.5 | 5.3 | 2821 |
| Macon | 9.8 | 5.8 | 2950 |
| Savannah | 8.7 | 5.7 | 2752 |
| Idaho |  |  |  |
| Boise | 12.4 | 4.0 | 3006 |
| Pocatello | 11.6 | 4.0 | 2864 |
| Illinois |  |  |  |
| Cairo | 10.9 | 4.8 | 2918 |
| Chicago | 10.1 | 4.3 | 2611 |
| Moline | 10.0 | 4.4 | 2563 |
| Peoria | 10.2 | 4.5 | 2673 |
| Springfield | 10.4 | 4.4 | 2702 |
| Indiana |  |  |  |
| Evansville | 10.7 | 4.3 | 2766 |
| Fort Wayne | 10.4 | 3.9 | 2570 |
| Indianapolis | 10.5 | 4.2 | 2668 |
| Terre Haute | 10.3 | 4.4 | 2675 |
| Iowa |  |  |  |
| Burlington | 10.8 | 5.1 | 2885 |
| Charles City | 9.9 | 4.5 | 2572 |
| Des Moines | 10.3 | 5.1 | 2770 |
| Sioux City | 10.9 | 5.4 | 2926 |
| Kansas |  |  |  |
| Concordia | 10.6 | 5.8 | 2916 |
| Dodge City | 11.2 | 6.6 | 3219 |
| Topeka | 9.8 | 5.2 | 2702 |
| Wichita | 10.8 | 6.2 | 3057 |

# At Home With Solar Energy

|  | Summer (Daily) | Winter (Daily) | Annual |
|---|---|---|---|
| Kentucky | | | |
| Louisville | 10.0 | 4.0 | 2601 |
| Louisiana | | | |
| New Orleans | 8.9 | 5.3 | 2744 |
| Shreveport | 10.8 | 5.6 | 3015 |
| Maine | | | |
| Eastport | 8.5 | 4.4 | 2309 |
| Portland | 9.7 | 5.3 | 2653 |
| Maryland | | | |
| Baltimore | 9.4 | 5.1 | 2653 |
| Massachusetts | | | |
| Blue Hill Obs. | 8.2 | 4.4 | 2257 |
| Boston | 9.4 | 5.2 | 2615 |
| Nantucket | 9.3 | 4.6 | 2585 |
| Michigan | | | |
| Alpena | 10.1 | 3.1 | 2324 |
| Detroit | 9.8 | 3.4 | 2375 |
| Lansing | 10.2 | 3.1 | 2378 |
| Escanaba | 9.4 | 3.9 | 2366 |
| Grand Rapids | 10.4 | 2.9 | 2406 |
| Marquette | 9.0 | 2.8 | 2104 |
| Sault Ste. Marie | 9.1 | 3.0 | 2117 |
| Minnesota | | | |
| Duluth | 9.6 | 4.4 | 2475 |
| Minneapolis | 10.2 | 4.6 | 2607 |
| Mississippi | | | |
| Jackson | 9.3 | 4.7 | 2646 |
| Vicksburg | 9.7 | 4.6 | 2705 |
| Missouri | | | |
| Columbia | 10.2 | 5.0 | 2757 |
| Kansas City | 10.5 | 5.3 | 2846 |
| St. Joseph | 10.2 | 5.1 | 2766 |
| St. Louis | 9.9 | 4.6 | 2694 |
| Springfield | 10.4 | 5.0 | 2820 |
| Montana | | | |
| Billings | 10.9 | 4.7 | 2762 |
| Great Falls | 11.1 | 5.1 | 2884 |
| Havre | 11.2 | 4.8 | 2874 |
| Helena | 10.5 | 4.7 | 2742 |
| Missoula | 10.5 | 2.9 | 2377 |
| Nebraska | | | |
| Lincoln | 10.7 | 5.6 | 2907 |
| North Platte | 10.4 | 5.9 | 2925 |
| Omaha | 11.1 | 5.6 | 2997 |
| Valentine | 11.1 | 6.1 | 3037 |
| Nevada | | | |
| Ely | 11.5 | 6.3 | 3211 |
| Las Vegas | 12.6 | 8.2 | 3838 |
| Reno | 12.8 | 6.2 | 3483 |
| Winnemucca | 12.1 | 4.8 | 3061 |

# Geography: Where You Live Makes a Difference

|  | Summer (Daily) | Winter (Daily) | Annual |
|---|---|---|---|
| **New Hampshire** | | | |
| Concord | 8.8 | 4.6 | 2354 |
| Mt. Washington Obs. | 4.8 | 3.1 | 1540 |
| **New Jersey** | | | |
| Atlantic City | 9.3 | 5.3 | 2683 |
| Trenton | 9.5 | 5.0 | 2653 |
| **New Mexico** | | | |
| Albuquerque | 11.1 | 7.3 | 3418 |
| Roswell | 10.7 | 7.3 | 3340 |
| **New York** | | | |
| Albany | 9.8 | 4.3 | 2496 |
| Binghamton | 8.2 | 3.2 | 2025 |
| Buffalo | 10.4 | 3.5 | 2458 |
| New York | 9.4 | 5.3 | 2677 |
| Rochester | 10.2 | 3.4 | 2392 |
| Syracuse | 9.6 | 3.1 | 2241 |
| **North Carolina** | | | |
| Asheville | 8.8 | 5.0 | 2646 |
| Cape Hatteras | 9.3 | 5.3 | 2669 |
| Charlotte | 9.6 | 5.6 | 2891 |
| Greensboro | 9.4 | 5.4 | 2767 |
| Raleigh | 8.8 | 5.3 | 2680 |
| Wilmington | 9.5 | 6.0 | 2919 |
| **North Dakota** | | | |
| Bismarck | 10.4 | 4.8 | 2686 |
| Devils Lake | 10.3 | 5.0 | 2714 |
| Fargo | 10.0 | 4.6 | 2586 |
| Williston | 11.0 | 4.9 | 2819 |
| **Ohio** | | | |
| Cincinnati | 10.1 | 4.1 | 2574 |
| Cleveland | 9.9 | 3.0 | 2352 |
| Columbus | 9.9 | 3.8 | 2508 |
| Dayton | 10.2 | 4.2 | 2664 |
| Sandusky | 10.4 | 3.5 | 2533 |
| Toledo | 10.0 | 3.4 | 2409 |
| **Oklahoma** | | | |
| Oklahoma City | 11.0 | 5.9 | 3048 |
| Tulsa | 9.9 | 5.4 | 2783 |
| **Oregon** | | | |
| Baker | 11.8 | 4.0 | 2835 |
| Portland | 9.3 | 2.6 | 2212 |
| Roseburg | 10.6 | 2.4 | 2283 |
| **Pennsylvania** | | | |
| Harrisburg | 9.8 | 3.4 | 2604 |
| Philadelphia | 8.9 | 5.0 | 2564 |
| Pittsburgh | 8.6 | 3.1 | 2202 |
| Reading | 9.0 | 4.6 | 2473 |
| Scranton | 8.8 | 3.9 | 2303 |
| **Rhode Island** | | | |
| Providence | 9.2 | 5.1 | 2589 |

111

# At Home With Solar Energy

| | Summer (Daily) | Winter (Daily) | Annual |
|---|---|---|---|
| South Carolina | | | |
| Charleston | 9.6 | 6.3 | 2993 |
| Columbia | 9.6 | 5.8 | 2914 |
| Greenville | 9.3 | 5.5 | 2822 |
| South Dakota | | | |
| Huron | 11.0 | 5.2 | 2844 |
| Rapid City | 10.5 | 5.4 | 2858 |
| Tennessee | | | |
| Chattanooga | 9.1 | 4.4 | 2591 |
| Knoxville | 8.8 | 4.2 | 2515 |
| Memphis | 10.4 | 4.7 | 2808 |
| Nashville | 9.6 | 4.3 | 2634 |
| Texas | | | |
| Abilene | 10.9 | 6.6 | 3137 |
| Amarillo | 11.0 | 6.8 | 3243 |
| Austin | 10.4 | 5.1 | 2790 |
| Brownsville | 10.2 | 5.0 | 2716 |
| Corpus Christi | 11.3 | 5.4 | 3003 |
| Dallas | 10.8 | 5.3 | 2911 |
| Del Rio | 10.1 | 5.8 | 2866 |
| El Paso | 11.2 | 7.8 | 3583 |
| Galveston | 10.0 | 5.0 | 2811 |
| Houston | 9.5 | 4.8 | 2633 |
| Port Arthur | 9.6 | 5.0 | 2768 |
| San Antonio | 10.0 | 5.1 | 2765 |
| Utah | | | |
| Salt Lake City | 11.8 | 4.7 | 3059 |
| Vermont | | | |
| Burlington | 8.9 | 3.4 | 2178 |
| Virginia | | | |
| Lynchburg | 9.2 | 5.3 | 2705 |
| Norfolk | 9.7 | 5.4 | 2803 |
| Richmond | 9.2 | 5.1 | 2663 |
| Washington | | | |
| North Head | 6.8 | 2.6 | 1783 |
| Seattle | 8.5 | 2.6 | 2019 |
| Spokane | 11.5 | 2.8 | 2605 |
| Tatoosh Island | 7.0 | 2.6 | 1793 |
| Walla Walla | 12.1 | 2.5 | 2685 |
| West Virginia | | | |
| Elkins | 7.8 | 3.7 | 2160 |
| Parkersburg | 9.0 | 3.3 | 2265 |
| Wisconsin | | | |
| Green Bay | 9.3 | 4.2 | 2388 |
| Madison | 9.9 | 4.2 | 2502 |
| Milwaukee | 10.0 | 4.0 | 2510 |
| Wyoming | | | |
| Cheyenne | 9.9 | 6.2 | 2900 |
| Lander | 11.2 | 6.6 | 3144 |
| Sheridan | 10.9 | 5.4 | 2884 |

Note: Computations of averages done by the author. Data from the U.S. Weather Bureau.

Why are these figures imprecise? For one thing, each number on the map is an average taken over a large part of the year. Also, each number refers to a large area. Local conditions that may strongly affect the actual value for each area are not taken into account, either. If you want to know the actual number of hours of useful sunshine for your area, you must consult tables of sunrise and sunset times for your area, then study years of meteorological data, computing averages and taking cloudiness into account. Fortunately, some of this work has been done for you. If you want to do a good part of the work for yourself, contact your local state agricultural extension service, or the local office of the U.S. Weather Bureau. Precalculated numbers might also be obtained from a local architect or company that installs solar energy equipment. Keep in mind, however, that these latter sources might not be objective about figures they present, since they both have something to sell.

There is a major factor in all this that you probably won't be able to find tables for, since it is unpredictable, in a state of flux, and constantly increasing. That factor is air pollution.

Air pollution is just as bad as clouds for solar collectors, since at the very least it cuts down on the intensity of the available sunlight; in some cities, at certain times of the year, pollution has been known to cut out the sunlight almost entirely. One estimate is that that the performance of a solar collector can be reduced by as much as 10 percent in New York or Los Angeles. That means that the collector size has to be increased to compensate for that loss in efficiency; if this isn't done, the homeowner will obtain less heat from his solar energy system, which in turn will mean using more conventional fuel to back up the solar system, and *that* in turn will mean a longer payback period for the solar equipment.

Now, most of us do not live in New York, Los Angeles, or some other heavily polluted city; but with the pollution from these cities spreading increasingly beyond their borders, and with even smaller cities now encountering the same problem more and more, the effect of air pollution on solar energy systems is rapidly becoming a nationwide problem, one that we should all worry about if we are thinking of solarizing our homes. Pollution levels

113

must be taken into account when deciding whether a solar energy system is economically practical for one's home.

This is a good place to define some of the terminology you're likely to run into if you hire an architect or solar energy company, or if you study some of the books listed as references in this book. Table 3 describes sunshine in terms of hours per day. But you may hear people talk instead of "langleys per day." To understand this you first need to understand calories and British Thermal Units (or Btu's, as this is usually abbreviated).

You may have heard Btu's used as a measure of the cooling power of an air conditioner, or the heating power of a heater. The Btu is a unit used to measure energy. One Btu is defined as the amount of heat needed to increase the temperature of a pound of water by one degree Fahrenheit. For example, if you have two cups (one pound) of water in a saucepan, and you increase its temperature from, say, 75 to 100 degrees Farenheit, you have put 25 Btu's of energy, in the form of heat, into it. In a similar way, the metric system defines its unit of energy, the calorie, as the amount of heat required to raise the temperature of one gram of water by one degree centigrade. (Centigrade and Celsius are the same.) This is indeed the same calorie that makes you fat: In food, the calorie content actually refers to energy the food would be converted into if you exercised. Without exercise, energy in the food is stored by the body in the form of fat. Since a pound of water is much more than a gram, and a degree on the centigrade scale is not even twice as much as a degree on the Fahrenheit scale, it takes much more heat to raise a pound of water by one degree Fahrenheit than it does to raise a gram of water by one degree centigrade. In fact, it takes about 252 times as much heat; therefore, one Btu of energy equals 252 calories of energy.

In designing a home solar energy system, one of the things one needs to know is how much heat a collector will absorb. The size of a collector determines how much of the sun's heat it will absorb. Just knowing the hours of useful sunlight isn't enough, since one hour of sunlight yields more heat in one location than another. (This is due to factors such as the height of the sun above the horizon and humidity, since water vapor in the air absorbs heat.)

Designers of solar energy systems use tables showing the amount of heat available from an hour of sunlight for a given city during a given month. Since it's important to raise the temperature of water (or air, or other fluid) in a collector to a desired temperature, it is necessary to know how many calories of heat will fall on the collector during an hour of sunlight. A *langley* is the amount of heat energy obtained when one calorie of heat falls on one square centimeter of surface area. If you know your city receives, say, 150 langleys of solar radiation during a typical December day, then each square centimeter of collector surface will receive 150 calories of heat energy during such a day. Since each calorie can raise one gram of water by one degree centigrade, the 150 calorie figure above lets you calculate how much collector area you need to keep the water in a solar energy system at a desired temperature. (You also have to know how much water a system would contain and how much water would circulate through the collector each hour.)

Earlier you learned about tables or maps of solar radiation expressed in terms of hours of useful sunshine. Such tables are also used for langleys, because local conditions such as humidity, pollution, and cloudiness, must be taken into account before solar energy calculations are made. Capable architects or solar energy companies take local conditions into account in their designs, but if you want to make rough calculations of your own, look at Figure 19, which complements Table 3 by showing average daily solar radiation in langleys for the United States for the middle of summer, as well as winter.

A heating system—solar or conventional—must be able to put out more heat in some parts of the country than in others, depending on how low temperatures become outside the house, and how long they tend to stay that low. One needs to know the *heating load* on a heating system—how hard the heater must work if it is to keep a house warm enough. For convenience architects give the concept of heating load a numerical value and speak of *heating degree days*. To come up with this number for a given city, first decide on the minimum inside air temperature for comfort. For example, set this temperature at 65 °F. We also need a table of

115

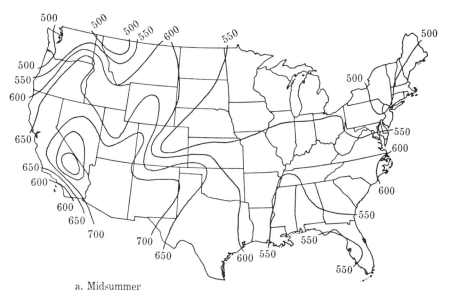

a. Midsummer

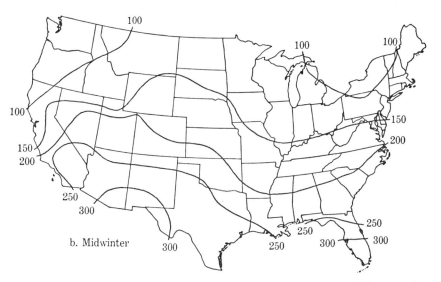

b. Midwinter

Figure 19—Average Daily Sunshine in the United States (in Langleys)
Source: U.S. Weather Bureau.

116

average daily temperatures throughout the year for this given city. For every day on which the average outside temperature is below 65 degrees, subtract that average from 65. Finally add the differences just computed, and the result is the heating degree days for that city. This number reveals the heating load a furnace or solar energy system (or combination of the two) must bear in that city to keep a house at a minimum temperature of 65 degrees. There are other factors to consider in the case of an individual house, such as the house's size, the R-factors of walls and ceilings, etc. But a map or table of heating degree days for various cities gives important comparative data. This also provides another figure that an architect or solar energy company must allow for in designing a solar energy system.

The same kind of calculation may determine the cooling load of an air conditioner. A base temperature for comfort is chosen (perhaps 75°F), then subtracted from the average daily temperature for each day that average *exceeds* the base temperature. The results are added. The sum is called the *cooling degree days* for that city. Tables of heating and cooling degree days may be found in the ASHRAE handbook mentioned earlier and at the end of this book.

As a rough idea of how heating degree days vary with location, the figure is under three thousand for the southern United States and over eight thousand toward the Canadian border. Combining this with the maps in Figure 19 shows why a solar energy system can provide only around 20 percent of a home's heat in the extreme northern United States: The heating load on the system is two and two-thirds greater than in the extreme South, but the amount of heat available from the sun to heat a house is only one-half to one-third as much.

*Additional Reading*

Powers, Edward and Witt, James. *Traveling Weatherwise in the U.S.A.* New York: Dodd, Mead & Co., 1973. Written for travellers and vacationers, rather than solar energy consumers. The book also has good summaries of weather patterns for

117

sections of the country, along with useful detailed pictures of weather in various cities.

Ruffner, James A. and Bair, Frank E., eds. *The Weather Almanac.* New York: Avon, 1979. Wealth of detail on local weather in the United States, including maps and definitions of heating and cooling degree days.

# ⑨ CONSERVATION: WHAT YOU CAN DO NOW

Even without using solar energy, there are many things you can do to your house to lower fuel bills. Some steps involve spending money, but savings in fuel bills often more than make up for the expense.

Energy-saving ideas were discussed in Chapter 6 in connection with the design of a new house. But some ideas from that chapter, such as the energy-saving effect of proper landscaping, apply to existing houses.

Insulation is very important in this respect, and has been given wide publicity lately as part of the government's push for energy conservation. Chapter 6 defined "R-factor" or "R-value," a measure of the insulating power of any insulating material. The R-values of adjacent layers of insulation may be added to show the R-value of the whole thickness of insulation. The amount of insulation you need depends on the climate where you live. As shown in Chapter 6, you may contact local government offices (such as your city or county building inspector) and local power companies to find out minimum R-values they recommend for walls, ceiling, and floors in your area. A quick guide is presented in Figure 20. Determine what heating zone you live in as shown on the map, then use the following table to determine the minimum R-values you should have on ceiling and floor:

119

| Heating Zone | Minimum R-Value | |
|---|---|---|
| | Ceiling | Floor |
| 0 | R-26 | R-11 |
| 1 | R-26 | R-11 |
| 2 | R-26 | R-13 |
| 3 | R-30 | R-19 |
| 4 | R-33 | R-22 |
| 5 | R-38 | R-22 |

Determining the actual R-value of your present insulation may not be simple. Insulation materials usually have an R-factor printed on them, but it is not necessarily reliable. R-values printed on insulation are correct when the material is new, but for various reasons, mainly compression of the layers of insulation, the real R-value of an insulation material decreases with age. You can get a better idea of the current R-value of your insulation by measuring its actual thickness and then using a table to find the R-value that thickness translates into. Tables for this purpose may be found in the handbook published by ASHRAE (American Society of Heating, Refrigeration, and Air-Conditioning Engineers) and in the United States government publication *In the Bank or up the Chimney?* (see the end of this chapter for ordering information), as well as in many other sources.

Depending on where it is to be placed, two types of insulation are generally used in houses: batts (or blankets) and loose fill. Batts, bought in thick layers, are tacked or stapled in place, while loose fill may be either poured or blown in. Different materials may be used in either case. Batts may be of glass fiber or rock wool, while loose fill may be glass fiber, rock wool, or cellulosic fiber. Batts are generally labelled as to the type of material in them, but for loose fill insulation, you may have to take a very small sample of it to a hardware store and ask someone to identify it for you. (If the material is not in the following table, you might also ask the hardware store if they have a table of the material's R-value as a function of thickness.) Find the material in the following table, then multiply the thickness of the insulation layer in your attic or basement ceiling by the appropriate number in the

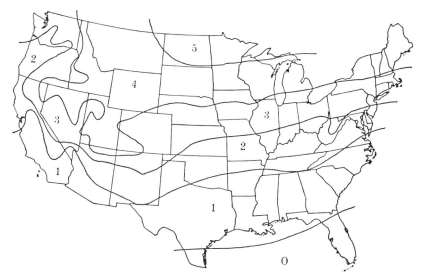

Figure 20—Heating Zones in the United States
Source: *Tips for Energy Savers* (U.S. Department of
Energy, 1978).

table. If you have 6 inches of cellulosic fiber loose fill insulation on
the floor of your attic, then the table gives you the number 3.7.
Multiply 6 by 3.7 and you get 22.2. Thus, the insulation in your
attic has an R-value of about R-22. Remember, R-values of different layers add up. Remember also that, if the floor of your attic
is finished, there is some insulation (probably loose fill) under the
floor boards. Short of taking up the floor, you can only guess at its
thickness and nature, but you could use 3 (for the number from
the following table) and the thickness of the floor itself as a rough
guess, then multiply for R-value.

| Batts or Blankets | | Loose Fill | | |
|---|---|---|---|---|
| Glass Fiber | Rock Wool | Glass Fiber | Rock Wool | Cellulosic Fiber |
| 3. | 3.7 | 2.2 | 2.9 | 3.7 |

121

This method gives only an approximation. The tables you will find in the publications mentioned above will give you more precise numbers. However, even the more precise numbers are only fully accurate for new insulation. If the subject seems annoyingly vague, you are unfortunately correct. The best anyone can do is try to help you guess whether money spent on insulation is justified in terms of money saved on heating bills. If your insulation is already adequate, you will not gain much by spending money on new insulation; if it is not adequate, you could be wasting a significant amount of money on fuel that heats outside air instead of your house. In this case, adding insulation could mean major savings.

Adding insulation is not as simple a matter as hardware stores pretend. You certainly do not want to try adding insulation to walls. Extra insulation in exterior walls can be helpful in some houses, but it is not a do-it-yourself project. It is definitely an undertaking for a professional contractor, a complicated business that can be very expensive. If you decide to have exterior walls insulated, be sure to contact a reputable contractor to do it for you, because horror stories abound of houses damaged by inept insulating contractors.

Floors and ceilings can be insulated by the do-it-yourselfer. Instructions are available in a variety of books, including the manual *In the Bank or Up the Chimney*, mentioned earlier. But if you decide to tackle this project, you must exercise a number of precautions. It is outside the scope of this book to give instructions for adding insulation, but here are a few of the main mistakes to avoid in such an operation.

Depending on where you live and the type of insulation, you may need to allow for a vapor barrier with your insulation; do not ignore this, for a vapor buildup can have serious consequences. When working in the attic, lay boards over the joists that form the floor, rather than standing on the floor boards between the joists; the floor there is the ceiling of the room below and will not hold your weight. If a chimney extends through your attic, make sure that nothing inflammable (such as the covering of batts or blankets) comes in contact with it. Also, leave at least three inches between insulation and any light fixtures; this is a situation you will encounter in the basement as well. Make sure not to block existing ventilation. You may be allergic to some types of loose fill insulation; if it's essential that you use one of these types, you must follow some precautions, such as keeping the material packaged until needed and wearing a protective face mask.

Drafts around doors and windows are a major problem in many houses. Such drafts can raise fuel bills winter and summer, by losing heat in winter and (in an air-conditioned house) letting heat in during summer. You can usually feel large drafts; you can use a candle to help find small ones by holding it near a suspected draft and looking for sudden, strong waverings of the flame. Weatherstripping for doors and caulking for windows is fairly cheap to buy and easy to install.

Storm windows are also a good investment, though their cost is considerably higher than caulking or weatherstripping. The best kind are custom-fitted to the house. A cheaper alternative, though not as effective at conserving heat, is plastic film, which you can tape to windows or put in wooden frames for mounting and removal. Along the same lines, look into modern versions of what used to be called venetian blinds. The modern version of this old standard is more attractive, and with proper slanting of the slats, it can be used to let in light without gaining heat in the summer, or losing heat in the winter. Interior wooden shutters can be used in much the same way.

Even if you don't choose to buy any of these installations for your windows, you can save energy by careful use of your existing draperies and windows. During winter, open draperies to let in direct sunlight, and close them on other windows, particularly those on the north side of the house. In summer do the opposite. During summer, if nights are cool in your area, open windows at night; close them in the day once the outside temperature climbs as high as the inside temperature.

Storm windows, mentioned above, work on the principle of using air trapped between the inside window and the storm

123

window as an insulating layer. Storm doors work the same way, but are not as effective as storm windows, because the doors are opened together with the inside doors, and the layer of air is replaced with cold outside air. Also, cold air moves into the house. If winds or the orientation of the house is wrong, much of the expensively heated air inside the building may be lost.

An expensive way around this is to have an entry lock installed. This means having two doors to the entrance, with a few feet between the two doors. If a house's design will accomodate it, it may be possible to add an extra doorway inside, behind the existing door. Otherwise, it would be necessary to add a protrusion to the outside of the house, covering the existing door and including the new outside door. The purpose of this arrangement is similar to that of an airlock in a spacecraft: to minimize the interchange of inside and outside environment. Only one of the two doors is opened at a time, so even under the worst wind and house orientation conditions, only a small amount of heated interior air escapes, and only a small amount of cold exterior air can get in. Similar benefits apply in summer, particularly if the house is air conditioned.

It's difficult to discuss the wisdom of having an entry lock installed. The cost depends on the nature of the existing house and the amount of work the homeowner is willing to do himself. The benefits from an entry lock depend much on local climate, winds, and house orientation, so one cannot even say much about it in general. An entry lock would be a nice thing to have, and your particular home might benefit greatly from one, but in most cases the cost of having one installed probably isn't justified by the saving on fuel bills. If you are building a house, however, talk the subject over with an architect, since an added expense at this stage may be small.

An idea related to storm windows and entry locks is the attached greenhouse. The usual version of this is a greenhouse built against the southern side of a house. This adds insulation, in the form of warmed air, in winter. By capturing the sunlight in the air and by shading the south wall, the greenhouse helps protect the house from heat during summer. An added benefit is the produce of the greenhouse itself. Some new houses have been designed with such greenhouses, and with ingenious arrangements of vents in the house's southern wall to allow interchange of air between house and greenhouse. Properly designed, this will increase the benefits of the greenhouse mentioned above.

As with an entry lock, a greenhouse large enough to be useful is not a minor undertaking. Generally speaking, it should be constructed only if you are interested in a greenhouse as well as saving fuel, and want to combine the two. Greenhouses have much to recommend them, especially in climates with short growing seasons, or, as is the case in most of the United States, temperatures so extreme during the year that tropical fruit trees cannot survive outside. If you plan to build a greenhouse anyway, you should consider the possibility of building it against the southern wall of your house.

You might also want to experiment with combining a greenhouse with an entry lock, if the orientation of your house and the position of your doors allows it. The potential problem here is that drafts of cold air coming into the entry lock may destroy the plants in the greenhouse! Careful design is essential.

Finally, here is a collection of ideas that involve far less expense than those above, or even no expense. You may have heard of some of these before, but they bear repeating because of their low cost.

First, the fireplace. While it's true that a cheerful, crackling fire adds a warm glow to a cold evening, the picture for your house and fuel bills is bleaker. A fire has to draw its fresh air from somewhere, and the ordinary fireplace draws it from the room. This increases the influx of cold air through cracks and chinks around doors and windows. Most of a fire's heat goes up the chimney, rather than out into the room, so the effect is a replacement of heated interior air with cold exterior air. In fact, the *net* effect in the average home of a fire in the fireplace is a *loss* of heat, and therefore a greater use of heating fuel than if the fire were not burning.

You can try various remedies. Fixtures at moderate cost may radiate more of a fire's heat into a room. These include reflective shields placed on the back walls of a fireplace, and a variety of devices for holding burning logs. These latter devices are designed so the metal heats up and radiates into the room. Newly installed fireplaces may be designed to do this without special fixtures. If you don't already have a glass front or screen for your fireplace, adding one will cut down on heat loss without reducing heat radiated out into the room by the fire.

A note of caution must be added. If your house is well sealed, or if you have just added caulking and weatherstripping to cut down on drafts, or if you are in the habit of closing off the room where a fire is burning to conserve heat elsewhere in the house, you could be in danger from the fire's fumes. If the fire cannot vent its fumes up the fireplace, then the air will circulate through the fire and back out into the room, carrying dangerous, potentially lethal gases. If you think this could be the case in your house, you should open a window slightly, near the fire, to establish a safe draft to carry gases out through the fireplace.

Always keep unused rooms closed during winter, and even close their heating outlets partially or entirely. This may not be practical in extremely cold climates, if items that could be damaged by cold temperatures are stored in those rooms. But in general, the less volume of air your furnace has to heat, the less fuel it will use.

A furnace will use less fuel if a house's thermostat is kept down. At night the thermostat can be turned down as far as it will go, if you have enough warm blankets to make up for it. If you are elderly, though, ask your doctor before lowering any thermostats, for you may be particularly affected by cold. Thermostats should be set as high as comfort will allow in summer, if you have air conditioning; if you live in a climate where the nights are cool and dry, you may be able to do without air conditioning at night, and open upstairs windows.

Your heating system must be kept operating as efficiently as possible. This is an area where money put into maintenance is more than paid back by savings on fuel bills. Your heating system should be cleaned and checked regularly by a professional (some experts say as often as once a year), and filters should be cleaned or replaced regularly. Heating ducts must not be blocked by furniture or other items. This also applies to air intake vents, which are sometimes treated as less important than outlet vents. If a furnace cannot get air through its intake vents, it cannot do a good job of sending heated air through its outlet vents. Remember, efficiency equals fuel savings, both in heaters and air conditioners. The higher the efficiency, the better.

An important savings connected with energy conservation is savings on federal (and in some cases state) income tax. Some energy conservation expenses—including the cost of insulation, caulking, weatherstripping, storm doors and windows, and others—may be used to reduce federal income taxes. You are allowed to claim a credit and reduce the income tax you owe by the amount of 15 percent of the money you spend on allowable energy conservation work, up to a total expense of $2,000 each year. Thus your maximum credit is $300. Note that this is a credit against taxes owed, not merely a deduction. This applies only to your principal residence.

Much of the energy-saving advice presented here is really common sense. It's sad that our neglect of good sense in energy use has helped get our country into its present crisis. We have taken the easy way—or what seemed the easy way at the time— for decades. As a nation, we are putting our famous ingenuity to work to search for alternative energy sources. We can immediately investigate at least one alternative energy source, solar energy. But we can do more: We can try our best to save the energy forms we now use. We are all in this together. America's energy crisis is not just Washington's concern—it's everyone's.

*Additional Reading*

*Complete Do-It-Yourself Manual.* Pleasantville, N.Y.: Reader's Digest Association, 1974. Covers insulation and fireplaces, along with virtually everything else you might want to work on in the house. Just one of many such books available from different publishers. Exceptionally clear and useful illustrations.

*Consumer Reports Money-Saving Guide to Energy in the Home.* Consumers Union. New York: Doubleday, 1978. Large, workbook format; useful. Consumers Union publishes the magazine *Consumer Reports.*

*In the Bank Or Up The Chimney?* The United States Department of Housing and Urban Development. Order from Consumer Information Center, Pueblo, Colo. 81009, attention R. Woods. Enclose check for $1.70 made out to Supt. of Documents, and mention catalog number 056G. Good book on energy saving, with heavy emphasis on insulation. Charts and worksheets help you estimate costs of various insulating devices and materials, for contractor installation or if you do the job yourself; and it will also help you estimate your savings. Contains fairly comprehensive instructions, if you want to do insulating yourself.

*Tips for Consumers Insulating Their Homes.* Order from Consumer Information Center, Pueblo, Colo. 81009. The free booklet covers types of insulation, tips on installing and buying insulation, and whom to contact with complaints.

*Tips for Energy Savers.* The United States Department of Energy, 1978. To order, write to "Tips for Energy Savers," Pueblo, Colo. 81009. The booklet has many suggestions for saving energy. (It's free.)

# 10 ECONOMICS OF SOLAR ENERGY

When a homeowner considers a major purchase the second question he usually asks is, "How much will it cost?" (The first question is, or should be, "Do I really need it?") Generally, solar hot water systems (those that provide hot water only, as described in Chapter 3) cost about $1,000, while complete solar heating systems (space heating, as in Chapter 4) average about $8,000. While inflation affects the solar energy industry like any other, causing increases in the cost of materials, labor, and distribution, the fairly steady increase in the market for solar energy systems has caused prices to drop. The net effect of these two competing trends will be to keep prices for solar hardware and installation at about the two figures given above for the next few years.

These estimates are still high enough to make most readers draw a deep breath and shake their heads. Conventional systems cost less to buy and have installed, and this has surely prevented wide use of solar energy in private homes. Solar energy is being used more on large government and corporate-owned buildings, for reasons that should become clear soon. A major factor in addition to initial (or "front-end") cost must be considered: *life-cycle costing.*

Chapter 4 explained that the idea in life-cycle costing is that one should consider not only an item's initial purchase price, but also maintenance and fuel costs for the item over its expected life. You should consider the actual *total* costs of an item over its entire useful life cycle, not just its initial cost. A car that gets good gas mileage, requires fewer repairs, and resells for more than another car might be a better buy, even if the latter car costs less initially. The car that costs more to buy might cost its owner less in the long run. Similarly, refrigerators are available which are designed to save energy and need less service. This is accomplished by better design, more insulation, and more careful manufacture. But the energy-saving refrigerator also costs considerably more to buy, and this has kept many consumers away. Over years of use, though, these refrigerators, by using less electricity, cost less to run than the standard variety. Their life-cycle cost is lower.

More must be considered in life-cycle costing than just the initial price and maintenance and fuel costs. Few of us can pay cash for a car; most are obliged to borrow money. Even when buying a refrigerator, many are forced to use a credit card—again borrowing, this time at up to eighteen percent annual interest. When performing a life-cycle cost analysis for two different items, one must be sure to include the extra interest paid on the more expensive item. Suppose you could buy either a standard refrigerator for around $500, or a similar refrigerator with energy-saving features built in, for about $800. Suppose you will finance either purchase with a department store credit card, meaning you will pay, in effect, eighteen percent interest per year. Finally, suppose you will pay the total cost off in three years. Over that three years, you will end up paying about $416 more *in interest charges alone* on the $800 refrigerator than the $500 one! From this view, the difference in initial cost is not $300, but $716, and *this* is the figure that should be used in life-cycle cost analysis. Actual dollar savings, in terms of lower electricity usage with the higher-priced machine, will vary from one part of the country to another, because the price of electricity is different in different areas.

In life-cycle costing, the useful life of the item determines its total operating cost. Although the above figures are correct as far as they go, the $800 refrigerator could be expected to last years longer than the $500 one. Therefore, you must also consider the cost of replacing the cheaper refrigerator. But enough of refrigerators. Back to solar energy equipment, where the situation, unfortunately, is more complicated.

This book will not give all the equations and tables that would enable you to perform a complete economic analysis of your house and the proper solar energy system for it. Extensive tables and equations can be found in the references given in this book, but even those are not of much use to the average homeowner, for he must first know many details about his house and its specific heating needs and heat loss characteristics, and the climate in his immediate area. This book instead uses averages, in the belief that these will let you decide whether to pursue the matter. The table given here should help you decide whether to consider solar energy for your home.

If you decide to solarize your home, or to look more deeply into the idea, don't rely on a solar energy company to make the final decision for you: Their attitude might not be entirely objective. It would be worthwhile to contact an engineering firm to give a solar appraisal of your house. Fees for this run about $100. It's a small investment, compared to the cost of a solar system for your house, especially if you buy the wrong system, or if you should not have bought a system at all.

The best way to contact such an engineering firm is to call the engineering department at a local university and ask for someone who can give you information on local firms who perform solar appraisals. You may find that the person you speak to at the university does such work himself on the side. You may also contact local offices of such organizations as ASHRAE (American Society of Heating, Refrigeration, and Air Conditioning Engineers), ISES (International Solar Energy Society), or any private group that lobbys for solar energy.

Such an appraisal will give you detailed information, since it will be tailored to your house and your location. This appraisal should serve as the final decision-making tool in any consideration of solarizing your house.

Chapter 4 referred to Figure 12 as illustrating the practicality of solar space heating in different parts of the country. Figure 12 shows the percentage of space heating that can reasonably be taken over by a solar system. Certain assumptions underlie these figures: a collector area of about five hundred square feet, a house of fifteen hundred to two thousand square feet area, and no extreme weather conditions for the house's site. If the house stands in a valley where cold air gathers, the percentage given in Figure 12 will be too high. Similarly, the percentage is affected by winds, pollution, and shade—factors discussed in Chapter 8. Another important factor is heat loss, which is assumed to be at a reasonable average. But if your house has poor insulation, or very good insulation, the percentage is wrong again. Details such as these will be covered by any proper solar appraisal, but the percentages in Figure 12 will suffice for this chapter.

By using Figure 12 and Table 4, you can get an idea of how long it would take a solar energy system on your house to pay for itself. You must first determine your total annual bill for space heating. This depends upon the type of heating your home has. If your furnace uses fuel oil, but everything else in the house runs on other fuels, then you may simply compute your total fuel oil bill for last year. However, if you use one energy source—say, electricity or natural gas—for space heating *and* other purposes, matters are more complicated. In this case, compute the bill for that fuel for any period when your furnace is not in use—for instance, the months of June, July, and August. Then multiply this total by the proper number—four, in the example given. Subtract the result from the total annual bill for that fuel. If you use natural gas for space and water heating, determine the annual space heating bill for your house this way: compute the entire year's natural gas bills, then subtract from that four times the total natural gas bill for June, July, and August. (The multiplication by four gives you the total money spent for the year on

Economics of Solar Energy

natural gas for all purposes other than space heating.) Once you have found the total spent last year for space heating, find the percentage given for your area in Figure 12, and multiply your annual space heating bill by that percentage. This gives you an estimate of the actual amount of money you could have saved last year on fuel bills had your house been solarized. You might want to make this estimate more precise by increasing the percentage from Figure 12 by five or ten percent if your house is small, well insulated, or well protected from cold winds. You might want to reduce the percentage by five or ten percent if your house is unusually large, or poorly insulated, or particularly exposed to cold winds, or is in an area of high pollution. Put this figure, the money saved on fuel by a solar energy system, aside for a moment.

Next try to gauge the percentage increase, year by year, in the price of the fuel you use for space heating. This is impossible to predict, of course, but you can estimate. Check your fuel bills for the last few years, comparing the cost per kilowatt-hour of electricity, or gallon of fuel oil, or hundred cubic feet of natural gas, from one year to the next.

Estimates suggest that energy prices will increase, nationwide, between 10 and 15 percent per year for quite a few years to come. However, if you try to guess at the economic impact of OPEC increases and domestic oil and natural gas deregulation, you can probably assume the increase will be anywhere from 15 to 25 percent per year! Most experts in the energy field have predicted annual price increases of at least 15 percent, and that may be conservative. In some areas of the country increases in fuel prices could be very moderate. This is particularly true in areas such as the Pacific Northwest, where much of the energy delivered to homes is hydroelectric, generated by dams. Supply there should not be a problem in the immediate future. Certain states have abundant supplies of natural gas and try to keep these supplies within their borders; residents of those states probably have little to worry about if they heat their homes with natural gas. For the majority of us, though, the outlook is rather gloomy.

133

Once you have decided on the right figure to use for the increase in your heating fuel costs, put that aside, next to the estimate on money saved by a solar energy system.

The final figure you'll need is the interest you would pay on a loan acquired for a solar energy system. That interest will depend on the length of time for the loan, security offered, and, perhaps most important, the place you go to borrow the money. Loans for solar energy equipment have been difficult to obtain; this is changing now, but you will probably still have to go to more than one organization before finding one that will loan the money you need. Presenting the information in this chapter cogently should help.

A solar energy system should last for twenty-five years, so you can think in terms of such a time span when arranging a loan. This means you can consider a second mortgage through a dependable organization, such as a bank, savings and loan company, or credit union. You can probably expect to pay less than 12 percent interest per year. You can consider a much shorter loan period than twenty or even ten years, and although this would mean higher payments, it would let you obtain lower interest rates.

You now have three figures—the amount you should save in a year using solar energy, the percentage by which fuel costs will increase per year, and the interest rate on a loan for solar energy equipment. You can now find, with the help of Table 4, the payback period for solarizing your home. The table gives you the number of years it would take for the savings in fuel costs to pay back the cost of the solar energy equipment, and the interest on the loan. Interest, as shown in the example of the two refrigerators, is a real part of the cost of the equipment, and should be included in life-cycle costing. Table 4 takes this into account, as well as the effect of incresing fuel prices. Your savings on fuel costs will increase each year as fuel becomes more expensive.

Many cautions need to be given about using Table 4. The numbers given in it are based on averages, including an assumed price of $8,000 for solarizing your home. (The table can also be used if another price is assumed; that will be explained shortly.)

134

Table 4.  Payback Periods (in Years) for Installation of Solar Equipment
(Initial cost - $8,000)

| Annual fuel cost increase | 10% | | | | 15% | | | | 20% | | | | 25% | | | | 30% | | | | 35% | | | | 40% | | | |
|---|---|---|---|---|---|---|---|---|---|---|---|---|---|---|---|---|---|---|---|---|---|---|---|---|---|---|---|---|
| Annual loan interest | 13% | 11% | 9% | 7% | 13% | 11% | 9% | 7% | 13% | 11% | 9% | 7% | 13% | 11% | 9% | 7% | 13% | 11% | 9% | 7% | 13% | 11% | 9% | 7% | 13% | 11% | 9% | 7% |
| Last year's fuel savings | Years | | | | Years | | | | Years | | | | Years | | | | Years | | | | Years | | | | Years | | | |
| $50 | — | — | 96 | 59 | 72 | 51 | 40 | 34 | 37 | 32 | 28 | 25 | 27 | 24 | 22 | 20 | 21 | 20 | 19 | 18 | 18 | 17 | 16 | 15 | 16 | 15 | 15 | 14 |
| 100 | — | 161 | 59 | 41 | 48 | 37 | 30 | 26 | 28 | 24 | 22 | 20 | 21 | 19 | 18 | 17 | 17 | 16 | 15 | 14 | 15 | 14 | 13 | 13 | 13 | 12 | 12 | 12 |
| 150 | — | 76 | 43 | 32 | 37 | 29 | 25 | 22 | 23 | 20 | 18 | 17 | 18 | 16 | 15 | 14 | 15 | 14 | 13 | 12 | 13 | 12 | 12 | 11 | 11 | 11 | 11 | 10 |
| 200 | — | 51 | 34 | 27 | 30 | 24 | 21 | 19 | 20 | 18 | 16 | 15 | 16 | 14 | 13 | 13 | 13 | 12 | 12 | 11 | 11 | 11 | 11 | 10 | 10 | 10 | 10 | 9 |
| 250 | 106 | 39 | 28 | 23 | 25 | 21 | 18 | 16 | 17 | 16 | 14 | 13 | 14 | 13 | 12 | 12 | 12 | 11 | 11 | 10 | 10 | 10 | 10 | 9 | 9 | 9 | 9 | 9 |
| 300 | 53 | 31 | 24 | 20 | 22 | 19 | 16 | 15 | 16 | 14 | 13 | 12 | 13 | 12 | 11 | 11 | 11 | 10 | 10 | 9 | 10 | 9 | 9 | 9 | 9 | 8 | 8 | 8 |
| 350 | 38 | 26 | 21 | 18 | 19 | 17 | 15 | 14 | 14 | 13 | 12 | 11 | 12 | 11 | 11 | 10 | 10 | 10 | 9 | 9 | 9 | 9 | 8 | 8 | 8 | 8 | 8 | 7 |
| 400 | 30 | 22 | 18 | 16 | 17 | 15 | 14 | 12 | 13 | 12 | 11 | 10 | 11 | 10 | 10 | 9 | 9 | 9 | 8 | 8 | 8 | 8 | 8 | 8 | 8 | 7 | 7 | 7 |
| 450 | 25 | 20 | 16 | 14 | 15 | 14 | 12 | 11 | 12 | 11 | 10 | 10 | 10 | 10 | 9 | 9 | 9 | 9 | 8 | 8 | 8 | 8 | 7 | 7 | 7 | 7 | 7 | 6 |
| 500 | 22 | 17 | 15 | 13 | 14 | 13 | 12 | 11 | 11 | 10 | 10 | 9 | 9 | 9 | 8 | 8 | 8 | 8 | 8 | 7 | 8 | 7 | 7 | 7 | 7 | 6 | 6 | 6 |
| 550 | 19 | 16 | 14 | 12 | 13 | 12 | 11 | 10 | 10 | 10 | 9 | 9 | 9 | 8 | 8 | 8 | 8 | 8 | 7 | 7 | 7 | 7 | 7 | 6 | 6 | 6 | 6 | 6 |
| 600 | 17 | 14 | 13 | 11 | 12 | 11 | 10 | 9 | 10 | 9 | 9 | 8 | 8 | 8 | 8 | 7 | 8 | 7 | 7 | 6 | 7 | 6 | 6 | 6 | 6 | 6 | 6 | 6 |
| 650 | 15 | 13 | 12 | 11 | 11 | 10 | 9 | 9 | 9 | 9 | 8 | 8 | 8 | 8 | 7 | 7 | 7 | 7 | 6 | 6 | 6 | 6 | 6 | 6 | 6 | 6 | 6 | 5 |
| 700 | 14 | 12 | 11 | 10 | 10 | 10 | 9 | 8 | 9 | 8 | 8 | 7 | 7 | 7 | 7 | 6 | 7 | 7 | 6 | 6 | 6 | 6 | 6 | 5 | 6 | 6 | 5 | 5 |
| 750 | 13 | 11 | 10 | 9 | 10 | 9 | 8 | 8 | 9 | 8 | 7 | 7 | 7 | 7 | 6 | 6 | 7 | 6 | 6 | 6 | 6 | 5 | 5 | 5 | 5 | 5 | 5 | 5 |
| 800 | 12 | 11 | 10 | 9 | 9 | 9 | 8 | 8 | 8 | 7 | 7 | 7 | 7 | 7 | 6 | 6 | 6 | 6 | 6 | 6 | 5 | 5 | 5 | 5 | 5 | 5 | 5 | 5 |
| 850 | 11 | 10 | 9 | 8 | 9 | 9 | 8 | 7 | 7 | 7 | 7 | 6 | 6 | 6 | 6 | 6 | 6 | 6 | 6 | 5 | 5 | 5 | 5 | 5 | 5 | 5 | 5 | 5 |
| 900 | 10 | 9 | 9 | 8 | 8 | 8 | 7 | 7 | 7 | 7 | 7 | 6 | 6 | 6 | 6 | 6 | 6 | 6 | 5 | 5 | 5 | 5 | 5 | 5 | 5 | 5 | 5 | 5 |
| 950 | 10 | 9 | 8 | 8 | 8 | 8 | 7 | 7 | 7 | 7 | 6 | 6 | 6 | 6 | 6 | 6 | 5 | 5 | 5 | 5 | 5 | 5 | 5 | 5 | 5 | 5 | 5 | 5 |
| 1,000 | 9 | 8 | 8 | 7 | 7 | 7 | 7 | 6 | 7 | 7 | 6 | 6 | 6 | 6 | 6 | 5 | 5 | 5 | 5 | 5 | 5 | 5 | 5 | 5 | 5 | 5 | 5 | 4 |

135

You'll probably find you fall somewhere in the middle of the table, so your payback period is about ten years. This means you could reasonably think of a loan period of ten to fifteen years, rather than twenty or twenty-five years; this means lower interest rates, so the table will give an even shorter payback period. If you have been assuming a fuel saving of $400 for last year due to solarizing your house, annual fuel cost increases of 25 percent and a loan interest of 13 percent, you will have a payback period of eleven years. However, if you were to reduce the loan interest to 7 percent by obtaining a shorter term loan, the payback period would drop to nine years.

In certain senses, the $8,000 mentioned above ends up being considerably less in reality. The most tangible reduction comes from the energy tax credit recently added to federal tax laws and similar laws in many states. On your federal taxes, you can receive a credit of 30 percent of the first $2,000 spent on installing solar, wind, or geothermal energy equipment on your house, and 20 percent of the next $8,000. (Thus the maximum credit is $2,200, if you spend a total of $10,000 on the equipment.) Note that this is a tax credit—it is subtracted from the taxes you owe, and is not just a deduction. The $10,000 maximum includes labor costs, not just the cost of equipment, so your tax credit is computed on the total real cost of the installation. This law applies to the cost of including a solar system in the design of a new house, and to the cost of solarizing an existing house, or retrofitting. Applying this to the $8,000 figure used to calculate the table, you will be able to get a credit on your taxes of $1,800 (assuming that your taxes for the year come to $1,800 or more). Thus, you could think of the system as costing $6,200, rather than $8,000. More states are passing similar laws covering state taxes, though some states reduce the amount credited on state income taxes by the rebate received from the federal government.

Other real financial benefits from a solar energy system that decrease the system's cost are higher home equity and interest payments deducted from taxes. Interest payment on the loan for a solar system is a tax deduction, and not a small one, if the loan is for $8,000. And like any other improvement, a solar energy system increases a house's resale value. A potential house buyer understands that a solar energy system, while it increases the price of a house, will also save him money while he owns the house.

On the negative side, your property taxes might go up because you add a solar energy system. States that have passed laws specifically concerned with solarized homes, however, usually exempt solar systems from increased property taxes. You should check the laws in your state; take into account the fluctuating status of such legislation, for politicians are late in waking up to the public's interest in and support of solar energy.

Another potential extra expense connected with a solar energy system is insurance coverage. A malfunctioning water-based system (see Chapter 2) can damage a home, and a roof-mounted collector visible from the street can be a target for vandalism. Your present insurance may already cover such matters; if not, it's worth the higher premiums to do so.

Chapter 7 discussed the technical feasibility of retrofitting a home, and the difficulties that might at least increase the cost of retrofitting dramatically. In general, as stated earlier, retrofitting should cost around $8,000. Similarly, $8,000 is a good estimate of the extra cost for solarizing the design of a new home. In special cases, the cost may be much more. Just what the actual cost would be for you can only be determined by a solar appraisal, as mentioned earlier in this chapter.

Suppose the cost of retrofitting your house with solar energy equipment will be about $16,000, or twice the average figure used to calculate Table 4. Assume the same data as before: fuel savings of $400 in the first year; annual fuel cost increase of 25 percent; loan interest rate of 13 percent. For a cost of $8,000, remember, the table gave a payback period of eleven years. For a cost twice that much, use a fuel savings for the first year of half the value used before, or $200. This gives a payback period of sixteen years. This is not as clear a figure as the eleven years obtained before; it's not as easy to decide whether retrofitting is worthwhile. The homeowner would have to take into account the age of the house and its expected usable life. Still, since the life of the solar equipment should be about twenty-five years, if the house will be habitable for sixteen years or more, retrofitting would seem to be a good investment.

For a more reasonable expense for retrofitting, suppose the cost is $12,000, or one and one-half the average used for Table 4, and that other parameters are the same as above. In this case, divide the $400 fuel savings by one and one-half. The result is $266.67; to use the table, round this off to $250. The table notes a payback period of fourteen years; retrofitting still seems a good investment.

In some parts of the country, the cost for solarizing could be considerably less than $8,000. If it were $4,000, with other figures in Table 4 the same, *multiply* the $400 fuel savings by two (since $4,000 is one-half of $8,000). The $800 fuel savings gives a payback period of seven years. In this case, solarizing would be a great investment.

In areas where the cost is lower, due to smaller collectors and storage tanks, the need for heating is also lower, because of greater sunlight and smaller heating degree days (see Chapter 8). For example, in the desert Southwest, a solar system can provide 90 to 100 percent of a home's heating needs, and the total cost of solarizing can be as low as $1,500 to $2,000—about the cost of a solar water heater in other parts of the country. As a result, the payback period is three years or less!

Generally, if you're in the upper left-hand corner of Table 4—a payback period of more than twenty years—you should not seriously consider retrofitting, and should think twice about solarizing even a new house. But if you're in the lower right-hand corner of the table, you should almost certainly solarize, whether that means adding to a new house or retrofitting. If you're anywhere else in the table, you probably should invest in a solar appraisal to see what is required in your particular circumstance. Perhaps the appraisal would show solarizing to be worthwhile for a new house, but might not show the same thing for retrofitting. The appraisal could come up with a much smaller fuel savings than you have assumed, or a retrofitting cost much greater than $8,000.

Chapter 1 discussed "net energy," the energy really obtained from coal, nuclear fission, or any other source, after the power used to obtain this energy is subtracted. Chapter 2 mentioned the related idea of "energy intensiveness," the amount of energy required to produce certain materials or substances, such as wood, aluminum, glass, etc., in the forms in which we use them. These two phrases may be combined under the general heading *energy investment*. This is the energy society must expend to produce an item for consumers, or to produce a material for manufacturers to use, or to produce energy from an energy source.

The money details discussed earlier in this chapter have a greater, or more immediate impact on your pocketbook than the factor of energy investment. But the needs of our society do count in the long run with most of us. From that point of view, according to one study, solar energy systems will pay back their energy investment in *less than one year!* That means that because of their low energy intensiveness and high net energy, solar energy systems, by saving large amounts of scarce fuel, will take less than a year to make up for the energy society must invest in their manufacture, installation, and maintenance.

No other energy source available, including nuclear fission, can make this claim. Apart from saving money or having a system that pays for itself, if you solarize your home you will certainly have a good reason to pat yourself on the back!

*Additional Reading*

*Buying Solar.* By the Federal Energy Administration. U. S. Government Printing Office. Washington, D.C. 20402. General and useful, with examples of solar appraisals. Order it from the Superintendent of Documents, above address (give the above title), and ask for Catalog No. 055G. Enclose a check for $1.85, made out to Superintendent of Documents.

Foster, William M. *Homeowner's Guide to Solar Heating and Cooling.* Blue Ridge Summit, Pa.: Tab Books, 1976. Interesting tables on economics of solarizing.
Kreider, Jan F. and Kreith, Frank. *Solar Heating and Cooling.* New York: McGraw-Hill, 1975.

# 11 SOLAR CON GAMES: PROTECTING YOURSELF

Solar energy was "born" about five billion years ago, but a sucker is born every minute. It often seems that a new solar energy company is born every minute, too, and this fact probably accounts for most of the problems consumers meet with solar energy. The explosion in the number of companies offering solarizing equipment for homes is a response to the upsurge of public interest in solar energy—especially to the public's willingness to lay down cash (or credit cards) for the equipment. Suddenly, many companies are interested in getting some of this "solar" money. You must avoid companies that are sincere but inept, as well as those that are dishonest, and choose one that is both honest and competent. This may not be easy, but this book can offer some guidelines.

If you have had a solar appraisal, as discussed in the last chapter, then the engineering firm that did your appraisal should be able to recommend a good company to provide equipment and install it. The appraisers may even be willing to choose components manufactured by different companies and arrange installation for you. But here you have the problem of being able to trust an appraisal firm beyond the appraisal itself. Are they objective, or is there a possibility of a kickback arrangement between the appraising engineers and the companies providing the hardware?

The last chapter discussed how you should choose an engineer-

141

ing firm to perform a solar appraisal. The guidelines mentioned there should help you avoid falling victim to the kickback arrangement mentioned above. You may apply the same guidelines to choosing a firm to provide solarizing equipment, or to checking up on the firm(s) chosen by an appraiser. As the amount of money involved in buying solar equipment is ten to one hundred times as much as the appraiser's fee, or even more, you should take even more precautions.

Before making any major purchase, whether solar or anything else, consumers should check with related offices and organizations to see whether the companies representing the products have had complaints filed against them by other purchasers. Contact your local Better Business Bureau. In virtually every state, the state attorney general's office has someone who deals with consumer fraud, and they should have lists of local companies to avoid. Most larger cities have some sort of consumer fraud office, and the same applies to many county governments. You should be able to find such an office in the telephone directory under state, city, or county offices. If not, there is normally a number given for information about state, city, or county offices not listed in the directory, and the information operator should be able to give you the right number. In many states, consumer fraud offices maintain toll-free telephone lines, so even if you live far from the state capital, you can call the consumer fraud office without paying. If your state government has no such office, or if its office does not maintain a toll-free long-distance line, then it is your right and your duty as a citizen to ask loudly, "Why not?" Consumer fraud protection is an essential and fundamental service of government; it is surely one of the reasons "governments are instituted among men."

Since we are dealing specifically with the purchase of solar energy equipment, there are other organizations you should contact before buying. The preceding chapter mentioned the local office of ASHRAE (American Society of Heating, Refrigeration, and Air Conditioning Engineers) and the ISES (International Solar Energy Society). You may also contact the Solar Energy Industries Association (your local office, or see the Appendix for the address of the head office in Washington, D.C.). ISES is a trade organization of companies that produce solarizing equipment of all kinds, and the organization has a certain obligation to support its members. Rumor has it that the association is compiling a blacklist of companies to avoid, though at the time of this writing, an ISES spokesman at the Washington office denied any knowledge of such a list. The organization seems to be well aware of its duty to safeguard the image of the industry; it's not clear whether this includes helping consumers avoid bad guys, even if those bad guys are members of the association.

The particular problem the consumer faces in the whole area of solar energy is that the business side of it is so young, thus firms involved in it are almost all new. This means many of them are not competent to install solarizing equipment, and that it is hard to evaluate them on the basis of their track record. Nevertheless, such an evaluation is still one of the acid tests.

Try to get the names of as many people as possible who have had their homes solarized by the company you are thinking of dealing with, and then contact those people. Ask them if the equipment works as claimed, and if they have had any excessive maintenance problems or costs, with the equipment itself or with getting the company to make repairs. Ask how long the people have had their systems—how many seasons it has been operating—and whether they have compared their present gas or electricity use to their use before the solar system was installed. Find out if their homes have suffered structural damage from the solarizing; if they don't know, suggest they check. As mentioned before, this sort of damage can happen if the company does not know its job (or is not honest), and it can represent a major hidden cost. Solarizing your house can involve much extra weight on the roof, some (possibly a lot of) excavation in your yard and/or under your house, and the installation of ducts throughout your building. If your system is air-based, the ducts are of large diameter. This spells potential danger to the structure of your house, and you need to be sure the company doing the work won't damage your building or do something that could lead to damage later. (Something else unpleasant to keep in mind: If the system is other

143

than air-based, it will usually involve toxic fluids, and any leaks, such as into your drinking water, will thus be very dangerous.)

Keep in mind the complexities of the law and its inadequacies in the area of solar energy. (These are discussed in Chapter 14.) Be sure the system to be installed does not violate local laws or covenants (restrictions imposed contractually, rather than legally, on additions to houses in a neighborhood). If your contractor is not aware of these potential problems, you may find yourself in legal difficulties for something *he* does. You should have his design for a solar energy system gone over by a competent lawyer who knows the legal aspects of solar energy. A lawyer should also check contracts or proposals worked out between you and a solar energy contractor.

Solar energy as a commercial field is young, and so is the effort by government agencies to collect data on fraud and customer dissatisfaction in this area. At the time of this writing, the amount of data available is very small, but what exists is enough to cause concern to potential consumers.

The Department of Energy in Washington, D.C. has tried for some time to gather such data. They have sent questionnaires to appropriate state, county, and city offices throughout the country, asking for information on solar energy frauds or related problems. To date, they have seen nothing to indicate widespread or systematic fraud. Apparently the decentralized nature of the industry, with, as yet, no solar energy version of General Motors or General Electric, means that fraud is also localized. The problem is to distinguish between intentional fraud and mere incompetence. Evidence of such incompetence among solar energy manufacturers and installers is distressingly plain.

By the time this book is published, there may be at least one centralized source for information on consumer problems in solar energy. During the spring of 1979, SERI (the Solar Energy Research Institute) gathered addresses of owners of solarized homes and asked for their comments on their experience with solarizing equipment. SERI had not announced plans to publish a "blacklist," but it might be worth contacting them at this address: Solar Users Information, SERI, 1536 Cole Blvd., Golden, CO

80401. In the meantime, you can learn about preliminary data collected by Marvin Yarosh and his associates at the Florida Solar Energy Center (kindly provided in unpublished form by Mr. Yarosh).

The Florida researchers used various techniques to obtain the names of owners of solarized homes throughout Florida. They dealt mainly with owners of hot water systems and solar pool heaters. The low heating load in Florida encourages people to continue to heat their homes with conventional fuels. In the future, solar cooling should become significant in this area of the country, but that must await the emergence of a more practical technology (see Chapter 5). Some homeowners told the researchers they had solarized cooling, but investigation revealed these were heat-pump-operated systems in some cases and conventional air conditioning systems in others. The owners *thought* their air conditioners were solarized, either because they had misunderstood the salesman or because the advertising was deliberately misleading.

A total of 86 percent of the owners (based on questionnaires) were "generally satisfied" or "very satisfied" with their equipment. Similar enthusiasm was expressed by those interviewed by other means. But here is the disturbing part. The Florida researchers visited many of the solarized homes and inspected the systems. They found that more than three-fourths of the installed systems had major present or potential problems. A majority of the owners of these defective systems were still pleased with their purchase! Some of the problems uncovered were serious. Systems were delivering virtually no hot water, and the backup conventional systems were doing all the work. There were systems so poorly installed that unsealed holes were left in the roof, and the connection between collector and house was inadequate. Some collectors were too small to do the job they were advertised to do, and some systems that were supposed to have freeze protection froze up during winter and became inoperative.

Similarly problems emerged when owners were questioned about warranty protection, written operating instructions provided them, and company response to problems. Yarosh and his associates feel the underlying cause of all this is not intentional fraud on the part of the solar energy companies, but rather inexperience, and poor training provided those who do the installing. The experience in Florida is an example of what is often called the "learning curve," a problem in most new industries. Matters should improve with time and public exposure. You will have to decide for yourself whether you feel this conclusion is justified. Meanwhile, the owners of the systems with problems, having paid substantial amounts of money for them, will eventually have to pay more to have their systems put in working order, or to have major repairs done to their homes.

The significance of all this to you is that there's a high probability of a bad job being done on any system you purchase, and you may not know how much faith to put in the responses of other owners you contact before you buy. However, if we step outside the area of solarized water heaters and into that of domestic space heating, the picture doesn't look quite so gloomy.

The Florida researchers concluded the reason those they surveyed seemed so unaware of the poor performance of their solarized water heating systems is that only about 20 percent of their home energy consumption goes to heating water, even if they have only a conventional system. The homeowners simply didn't notice the small increase in fuel use if their solarized water heater stopped working. Since the residents of the houses had hot water when they needed it, they assumed their solarized systems were working, when in some cases all hot water was being provided by the conventional backup system!

In most of the country space heating uses two or three times the 20 percent of home energy mentioned above. So the effect of a nonworking solarized space heater would show up immediately in utility bills. The small amount of data concerning solarized space heating collected by the Florida researchers shows a much lower rate of satisfaction. The same is true of solarized pool heaters, where there is no conventional backup system, and any inadequacy of the solarized system is immediately obvious. All this must be borne in mind if you contact homeowners who have bought from the company you are thinking of dealing with. If the homeowners are enthusiastic about the product, does their home have only a solarized water heater? If so, view their enthusiasm with skepticism. If they have solarized space heating, ask if they have compared the amount of electricity or natural gas used during winter to the amount used during previous winters (taking into account that all winters are not the same). If the solarized heater has cut down on energy use, does the amount saved seem reasonable in terms of Figure 12 or the savings claimed by the solar energy company? Finally, suggest that the homeowners try turning off their conventional backup during cold weather (if they can do so) to see what happens when the entire load must be carried by the solarized space heater.

Ask the owners if they have been given operating or troubleshooting instructions by the company, and if so, how clear and extensive the instructions are. Ask if they have found the company cooperative about repairing or replacing any malfunctioning components. And ask what sort of warranty they were given.

Virtually all manufacturers of any kind of mechanical equipment provide some sort of warranty, but warranties are almost always carefully worded so they seem to say more than they do. The best warranty is one that is limited as to the problems it covers but specifically states just what those problems are and just what the company is obligated to do about them. In this case, the company has not made a grandiose claim that implies you need never worry about its product breaking down, or perhaps guaranteeing it only to be one of the best of its kind. Instead it has listed certain problems (such as corrosion in the case of a water-based system) that can happen in even the best-made equipment, and the company has promised to repair such damage at no charge to the homeowner. If you are already paying a lawyer to look over a contract or other agreement for solar equipment before you sign it, it wouldn't hurt to have him look at the company's warranty and comment on it. Lawyers' fees are not low, but for work of this kind, the fee a lawyer will charge, like the fee charged by the solar appraisal firm, is a cheap way of avoiding an $8,000 mistake.

## At Home With Solar Energy

Your best defense against confidence games and ineptitude is background knowledge, such as this book tries to provide, common sense, and healthy cynicism. One claim by any solar energy company that should immediately sound alarm bells in your mind is the claim that they can do what you *know* is too much.

Preceding chapters should have given you a fairly good idea of what solar energy can do for a house. Based on this, you should be suspicious of any company that claims to be able to do a great deal more than that for your house. The most obvious claim to beware of is that this company's system on your roof means you will never again have to turn on your furnace. This could be true in a few locations, but you have probably concluded from previous chapters and from experience of your local climate that this would not be true where you live. Even if the company does not claim their system will provide all of your home's heating needs, the percentage they claim for their system may seem suspiciously high. You should be wary of this, too. Here again, a solar appraisal will have armed you beforehand with specific knowledge, tailored to your house and area, to protect you against extravagant claims. If you have contacted other owners of the company's system, you will be able to use that information to also decide whether the claims are extravagant. (If the company is not new and there are no other homes in your area with the company's system installed, then this is a warning flag by itself!)

Here is an example of an excessive claim, uncovered by workers at the Florida Solar Energy Center. In 1976, advertisements appeared in Florida and elsewhere for a solarized swimming pool heater with, apparently, remarkable abilities. According to the advertisement, a single collector array, attached to an average size swimming pool, could raise the temperature of the pool's water by 5°F or more; for an increase of 10°F or more, the ads said to simply buy and install two collector arrays. According to Energy Center tests and calculations, even assuming the best operation of hardware and the most favorable weather conditions, the very best one could hope for with the equipment would be an increase of less than one tenth of the amount advertised. This was surely a case of fraud rather than ineptitude.

148

Companies have also advertised collectors that can heat a pool year-round; in fact, this would only be possible with enormous, and enormously expensive, collectors. Others have advertised hot water systems said to save specified amounts of money on utility bills. But the amount a family saves depends upon family size and water use habits.

Even with the best of intentions, the highest standards of honesty, and the most competent designers and installers in the business, a solar energy company can go out of business, leaving owners of its systems high and dry when they need repairs or replacements. This can happen in any industry, but it is a particular problem in the solar energy industry, where new companies appear as rapidly as mushrooms, filled with enthusiasm but without the capital to withstand temporary business adversity. About three fourths of the solar energy companies now in business are less than three years old, and it's hard to guess how many of those companies will still be in business five years from now—when you might be in desperate need of repairs or replacements for your system.

You can also use company longevity as a criterion for choosing the firm you deal with. This has an element of unfairness in it, unfortunately. A new company may grow within the next few decades to become the General Motors of its industry; based on the record, it doesn't seem likely. The year 1977 was a benchmark for the industry. During the early and mid-1970s, growing enthusiasm for solar energy led to the formation of a vast number of small companies—much the same as the process we see now. Then matters slowed suddenly, and 1977 saw a wave of corporate deaths. Companies still operating successfully that were in business at the beginning of 1977, having survived that disastrous year, are companies that probably have the best chance of being around when you need them.

This is purely a matter of corporate stability, of sound business practices, adequate capitalization, and reasonably steady sales—not a matter of honesty or technical competence. However, laying aside the question of whether a dishonest and/or incompetent company can survive a depression in its industry, the important point is that if a company has survived to the present since 1977, it will probably survive in the immediate future, given the much brighter outlook for the solar energy industry. You should ask the age of the solar hardware company you're planning to buy from, and should not let yourself be overly impressed by the company's enthusiasm, its hopes for the future, or its belief that it has solved the technical problems of solar energy in a way no one else has thought of.

For a list of companies selling solarized products and an explanation of how these companies were selected for mention (primarily by the age criterion explained above), see the Appendix.

## Additional Reading

*Buying Solar.* (See list of books at end of preceding chapter for more information on this publication.)

*Homeowner's Guide to Solar Heating and Cooling.* (Also find this in book list at end of preceding chapter.) Chapter 8 of this guide has advice for consumers from a somewhat different slant than the one taken in this book. Since the emphasis is on buying, installing, and maintaining a solarized heating or cooling system yourself, rather than having it done for you, much of the advice is in the area of technical details that solar appraisers and lawyers will handle if you pay for professional help.

# 12 UNCONVENTIONAL SOLAR HOMES

This chapter and the next cover subjects not directly applicable to the consumer side of solar energy, but will interest readers whose tastes run to the experimental or unconventional.

So far this book has considered conventional houses—conventional, except for the addition of solar energy hardware. Most Americans, upset as they may be by high fuel bills and therefore interested as they are in solar energy, would probably still prefer to live in a house that doesn't look too odd. Architects have learned to design solarized houses that look fairly conventional; the only hardware that need show from the outside is a bank of collectors, and *they* are now being made to look almost handsome.

There is a drawback to imposing conventional appearance on a solarized house, or on *any* house. Earlier methods of house design took account of local climate to enhance heating and cooling. The "efficiency" and standardization in modern mass construction methods ignore local climate. Unconventional, experimental houses designed to maximize use of the outside environment for the comfort of the house's residents are interesting as a means of gaining useful information about new design ideas; but they may also be prophetic, showing how we, or our descendants, will live in the next century.

151

Experimental homes have sprung up all over the country in recent years, incorporating new knowledge of solar-oriented design. One such home will be described later in this chapter.

The three "pioneer" solar houses described in this chapter demonstrate what is usually called "passive design," or "passive solar design." Passive design consists of several methods whereby a house can use the sun's energy with as little hardware as possible. Fans, pumps, and the array of hardware and moving parts you would expect to see in a solarized house are avoided, as far as possible. In passive design, no outside energy (such as electricity to drive pumps or fans) is used. Normally, there is no flow of fluid; if there is, gravity is used to do the work, in conjunction with the tendency of warm fluids to rise. Ignoring the matter of heated fluids, you can perhaps see that passive solar design is really what was talked about in Chapter 6, and to a lesser extent in Chapter 9.

The appeal of passive design is that it is cheaper to incorporate passive principles into a new house than to include the hardware described in the first chapters of this book. The hardware that may be used in some passive design schemes is simple and cheap, and generally requires much less maintenance than other solar energy equipment. It also requires no outside energy. But in most of the country, passive design simply cannot save as much energy as systems using the other hardware. Also, to realize the full potential of passive design means living in houses like the ones you will now read of, and few people are willing to do that. Conventional houses meet building codes and covenants more easily than experimental homes, and are far easier to buy or have built, or to finance. The government has apparently decided to push passive design ideas, though that doesn't mean it will push the hardware described in this book any less.

Experimental house number one illustrates a device called a *roof pond*. This is basically a thick layer of water on the roof, which performs the same function as solar collectors described earlier in this book. In this case, though, there is no storage tank for the heat, and no piping or ductwork. Water on the roof acts as collector and storage tank, and stored heat is radiated directly through the roof and into the house. The layer of water is also used for cooling during summer.

The pioneering example of a roof pond was designed and built by Harold Hay and John Yellot in Phoenix in 1967. They built a one-room, single-story house with adjoining carport, covering a total area of ten by twelve feet. (This was only a prototype.) The men placed black plastic sheets between roof beams to create water ponds seven inches deep. Above all this they placed three urethane insulation panels, which could be slid away from the water, exposing the ponds to the sky, or slid back in place over the water. The panels moved by means of a pulley system operated from inside the house. The idea is illustrated simply in Figure 21.

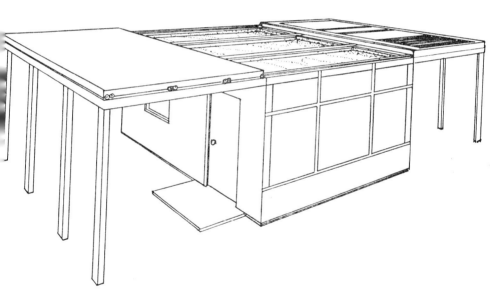

Figure 21—An Unconventional Home (Harold Hay's)

During winter, the panels were slid away during the day, so the ponds could be exposed to the sun and gather heat. At night the insulation was moved back over the water to retain heat, which was radiated through the roof into the house. During the time the

153

house was monitored by the two investigators, the coldest it got inside was 68°F. Most of the time it was no colder than 70°F.

In summer the pattern was reversed. The ponds were exposed during the night so water would evaporate and therefore cool. In the day, the ponds were covered again, so water could not warm in the sunlight. The effect was to cool the house, since the layer of cool water on the roof absorbed heat from inside the structure. The warmest it got inside was 82°F, and most of the time it stayed below 80°F. (This was in Phoenix, where outside summer temperatures are 105°F or more most of the season!) The water provided an important insulating effect in all seasons.

Encouraged by this success, Hay designed a more elaborate house. He was able to build the newer version at Atascadero, California in 1973. This version is also a single-story house; with a roof pond, all the living space must be under the roof to receive heating and cooling effects from the water. This house also has a carport. Heated floor space within the house amounts to 1,100 square feet. The water is actually contained in huge plastic bags, rather than being exposed directly to the air. While evaporation enhanced the cooling of the water, it also used up too much of it in the Phoenix test house, even with a plastic cover added. In the California version, evaporation was avoided from the beginning. About seven thousand gallons of water form ponds eight inches deep above the living space. This means a huge weight, for which sturdy support is provided. Extra protection is also provided against leakage. And because of the house's location, the roof is designed to be earthquake-proof.

The carport houses a car and provides storage space for the roof's movable insulating panels. When the panels are not covering the water ponds, they are slid off to the side and stacked on the carport's roof. The panels are not manually operated, as they were at the Phoenix test house, but are moved by small electric motors hooked up to thermostats and automatic controls, so residents of the house need never think about the position of insulating panels. The principle is the same as the Phoenix version, with heating and cooling accomplished in the same way. The California version, however, in addition to being larger than the

154

Phoenix test home and having such refinements as the automatic controls, is designed as a real home and not just a test structure. It is said to look like any other suburban house when seen from the street, since from that viewpoint the roof ponds are not visible.

The temperatures experienced during summer and winter at the California house are similar to those at the Phoenix house. An advantage of the Hay house over houses with conventional heating and/or air conditioning systems is the lack of noise—the Hay house has no fans or other blowers. The roof pond system is cheaper to build and maintain than other solar energy systems (the non-passive variety), and in climates like those of Phoenix or California, it deals remarkably well with the weather.

A similar idea that has been put into practice with impressive results is to have the water collectors in the walls instead of on the roof. Perhaps the most striking and most widely known example of this is our experimental house number two, which features the "Drumwall" design used by Steve Baer in his house near Albuquerque, New Mexico. One view of this unique dwelling is shown in Figure 22.

Baer calls this wildly shaped building his "zome," a contraction of "zoned home," because it is designed as a collection of separate modules, or zones. As you can see from the figure, which presents a south view of the "zome," the south-facing walls are covered with shutters, or insulating panels similar to those on the roof of Harold Hay's home. These panels can be lowered to expose the walls themselves; this is where the innovation appears. The walls actually consist of arrays of fifty-five gallon drums (thus, Drumwall) filled with water. (They are the circular objects in Figure 22.) Each zone has twenty to twenty-five of the drums, and each drum has an outside surface painted black and inside surface painted white. A wall of double glass is between the drums and outside air; if this were not so, outside air would move through the space around the drums, and the effect of heated or cooled water would be lost.

155

Figure 22—Another Unconventional Home (Steve Baer's "Zome"). Photo: Zomeworks, Inc.

The operation of the Baer house is similar to that of Harold Hay's house. Shutters prevent loss of heat from the barrels during winter nights, and expose the barrels to the sun on winter days. In summer the drums are exposed at night, so the water will cool by radiation into the desert night sky. Shutters are raised on summer days to keep the drums from heating. As in Hay's house, the home is cooled by water.

Baer's house has some additional features. The house is covered with a reflective aluminum skin, which insulates against sunlight during the summer. The aluminum reflects sun in winter, too, but exposing the black-painted water drums more than compensates for this heat loss. The exterior faces of the drums are vertical, not the optimum angle for exposure to the sun. To compensate for this, the inner surfaces of the shutters, also aluminum, are highly reflective. When the shutters are completely open, they are flat against the ground, and reflect much sunlight onto the barrels. The shutters are hand operated, but the "zome" also has an automatically operated, louvered, opaque skylight, which opens to allow in sunlight, and closes to prevent heat loss.

To complete the sun-oriented living style, the Baer "zome" has two solar water heaters and a windmill-operated well pump. (Wind is caused by solar heating of the atmosphere, and therefore, by a slight stretch of definitions, is also a form of solar energy.)

Baer's experience with temperatures inside the house is similar to that described earlier for Hay, though Baer's "zome" requires auxiliary heating.

Baer is also the designer of the Beadwall, an ingenious window that can easily be made either transparent, to let in sunlight, or opaque, with a high R-value to insulate against heat loss or too much heat gain. The Beadwall consists of two parallel panes of glass—or plastic, or any other appropriate transparent material that might be discovered in the future. When insulation is needed, polystyrene beads of a small diameter are blown into the space between the panes. (A three-inch thickness of these beads has an insulating value of about R-10.) When sunlight is desired, the beads are sucked into storage by vacuum cleaner motors, and the Beadwall again becomes a simple double-paned window.

If you are interested in Baer's work, or in buying a Beadwall or plans for a "zome," write to Steve Baer, Zomeworks Corporation, P.O. Box 712, Albuquerque, New Mexico 87103.

Experimental house number three is a recently built house just north of Denver, Colorado. You will recognize its main features immediately.

The house, called the Sunearth House, was designed and built by Paul Shippee of Colorado Sunworks in Boulder, Colorado. It uses a Beadwall, a Drumwall, and earth berms, or ledges, around and above the building. Since even the roof is covered with a foot and a half of soil, the house is under ground, except for its south wall. This provides superb insulation, protection from strong winds of the area, and even insulation against traffic noises from a nearby highway. The south wall is essentially a Drumwall, as in Baer's "zome," but without the shutter arrangement. Part of the south wall is given over to a Beadwall, as described above. Concrete was used liberally in the structure, for its insulating and heat-retaining abilities. The entrance to the house is in the form of an entry lock, as described in Chapter 9. The fireplace draws its air from outside rather inside the house, so its net effect is to heat rather than cool the interior. (Chapter 9 explained how most conventionally designed fireplaces cool a house more than they heat it.)

There are other, minor design innovations in the Sunearth House, but let us see what effect all this solar-oriented design has on fuel bills (some conventional auxiliary heat is needed). During a recent cold winter in Colorado, the total hot-water bill for the house was $9 for December *and* January. The furnace was never used! (The interior living area is eighteen-hundred square feet, larger than the average house.) The cooling effect of the insulation and Drumwall is just as impressive: With the temperature close to 90°F outside, the inside of the house remains just above 60°F.

158

Intriguing as all of these homes are, they have one striking feature in common—their geographic location. They are all in the West and Southwest, in areas where the total heating load is not severe, and sunlight is abundant (see Fig. 12, 19, 20; Table 3). It is not clear that these passive systems would perform as well in other parts of the country. Some attempts have been made to combine modifications of these ideas with partially active systems in colder areas, and the results are encouraging. Passive systems are still at the do-it-yourself stage, since they are not commercially available in the same way that active solar systems are. But the concepts underlying passive systems are worth considering in the design of any new house. If you are interested in do-it-yourself solar projects and live in a favorable climate, you should think of tackling a passive design project before undertaking one of the active designs.

## *Additional Reading*

Alves, Ronald and Milligan, Charles. *Living With Energy.* New York: Penguin Books, 1978. Primarily a picture book, showing many alternative houses with active and passive solar energy systems.
Anderson, Bruce. *The Solar Home Book.* Harrisville, N.H.: Cheshire Books, 1976. Chapters 4 and 5 discuss alternate passive designs, including the Hay and Baer houses, and other houses that embody and extend Hay's and Baer's ideas.
Skurka, Norma and Naar, John. *Design for a Limited Planet.* New York: Ballantine Books, 1977. A general book on the need for alternatives to fossil fuels, with many pictures of unusual home designs using energy-conscious ideas.

# 13 SOLAR CELLS

During the last twenty years, we have become accustomed to seeing drawings and photographs of spacecraft with wing-like structures. These arrays are solar cells that power the vehicles by generating electricity from sunlight. During the 1973 Skylab missions, the astronauts' space habitat had to operate on reduced electrical power when one of its "wings" failed to open fully during the vehicle's earth orbit.

Because of the popularity of the space program during the 1960s and early 1970s, much interest was created in these solar cells, and predictions were made that such devices would some day power our houses. Arrays of them, sitting on the roof, would provide all the electricity anyone could desire. Obviously that has not happened. It is not likely to happen for many years, for reasons that will be discussed in this chapter. But the prospects for solar cells are still exciting in the long run.

In 1887, German physicist Heinrich Hertz noticed that electrically charged subatomic particles called electrons could be made to escape from metal if a light of sufficiently high frequency was shone on the metal. This phenomenon came to be called the "photoelectric effect," but even though it had a name, no one knew what caused it. It was not until 1905 that an explanation of the photoelectric effect was published by Albert Einstein. (Einstein won his Nobel Prize for Physics in 1921 for his work on the

160

photoelectric effect, and not for his Theory of Relativity, for which he never did win a Nobel.)

For ordinary metals, the frequency of the light that shines on the metal has to be extremely high, and the number of electrons produced is not very great. Electrons can be thought of as constituting electric current, and much effort has been expended for decades in trying to increase the amount of current generated in this way, and also to find substances that generate electricity when exposed to light frequencies easily obtained in nature—in sunlight.

Because of our understanding of the photoelectric effect provided by Einstein, it became possible to move beyond ordinary metals and construct special layered crystals of substances that generate far more electricity than any metal when exposed to sunlight. This is the source of both the advantages and drawbacks of the modern solar cell, also called a "photovoltaic cell" or "photoelectric cell." Not only do the substances used have to be in layers of proper thickness, but the substances themselves have to be of the proper "doped" crystal structure. This means the atoms of the substance have to be in the right geometrical relationship, and atoms of other substances have to be inserted into this geometrical arrangement in the right places. (The term *crystal* refers to the basic geometric arrangement, while the presence of other substances, or impurities, in the crystal structure is called *doping*.)

In order to improve the cell's production of electricity, great care must be taken with its manufacture. This is true even down to the level of the geometric arrangement of atoms of the substance and atoms of the doping materials. Originally this meant all such cells were enormously expensive. Moreover, because of the relatively primitive manufacturing technology available years ago, the cells could not generate a satisfactory electric current from available sunlight. This meant even more expense if electricity was to be generated, since even more of the costly cells would be needed.

These facts defined two lines of attack. One was to find cheaper manufacturing methods that would still yield satisfactory cells.

161

The other was to find substances and designs that would improve the performance of solar cells. How well both approaches have succeeded can easily be illustrated.

For many years, most solar cells were made of silicon. Silicon is one of the most abundant elements in the earth's crust, but it has to be purified to a great degree before it can be used to make solar cells. This has historically made it very expensive. Because of improving technology and increasing demand, the cost of purified silicon dropped from $400 per pound to $80 per pound by 1961. The price has continued to drop since then, but materials other than silicon have become popular for solar cells. Simultaneously, new methods of manufacturing the cells have appeared, also lowering the cost of cells.

The efficiency with which a cell converts solar energy into electrical energy must also be considered. Some frequencies of sunlight are effectively useless to a solar cell; other frequencies cause the cell to operate quite inefficiently. The best that could ever be expected of any solar cell is 45 percent efficiency— less than half of the sunlight shining on the cell would be converted into electricity. For reasons having to do with the structure of the cells and nature of the electricity generated by a solar cell, not much more than half this efficiency may be expected. In the early 1950s, the best anyone had managed with solar cells was about one percent efficiency. By the mid 1950s that amount had risen to about 11 percent. Ten years later, almost 15 percent efficiency was being reported, and by 1977 that figure had risen to 22 percent. We have reached what seems to be the expected limit.

Such limits have been proclaimed before in the history of science, and those who proclaimed them have later been made to look foolish by a dogged scientist who refused to accept any limits. That may prove to be the case with solar cell efficiency. However, the percentage of efficiency is not the number we need to concern ourselves with most. The number that counts, from the point of view of this book, is the actual cost of the electricity delivered by the cell. This cost is found by combining the efficiency of a cell with its cost of manufacture.

## Solar Cells

In 1961 solar cells made from silicon could generate electricity at a cost of about $175 per watt. This figure for a solar cell is normally given for "peak watts," assuming the solar cell is exposed to the sun at noon on a cloudless day. In that sense, it is the cost when the cell is performing at the best possible rate. Most of the time the cell is really generating electricity at a higher cost. Still, the peak-watt concept provides a handy way to compare types of cells and the progress of solar cells over the years. You pay the utility company for electricity by the kilowatt-hour, so a direct comparison between what you pay and what a solar cell costs can't be made. The general feeling among experts, however, is that solar cells will become competitive with utility-generated electricity for the home when a solar cell can produce electricity for fifty cents per watt. Some say it could be as high as one dollar per watt, particularly after electricity rates continue their rise for a few more years.

By 1978 silicon cells had dropped to about $12 per watt. At this point, materials that promised to deliver much cheaper electricity than silicon cells began to appear. Many of these newer cells involved different designs and structures, in addition to different materials. One type, made from cadmium sulfide and copper sulfide, should drop to $2 per watt by the early 1980s and, its supporters feel, about twenty cents per watt within ten years after that. That would easily make the cell competitive with electric utilities.

We may not have to wait until the 1990s, however. In the late 1960s, a type of silicon-based solar cell was developed that did not even require silicon in a crystal structure. Called "amorphous silicon" or "amorphous semiconductor" cells, these devices have generated great enthusiasm. Assuming proper market conditions, these cells should be generating electricity at fifty cents to one dollar per watt by the early 1980s. If this promise is fulfilled, the solar cell will have become quite attractive. The amorphous silicon alloy from which these cells are made has another advantage over the crystalline silicon from which the older type of cell is made—its durability. Solar cells have always been highly susceptible to degradation over the years, due to scratches and physical

163

and chemical changes within the cell. The cells' efficiency drops as they age, and soon they are producing so little electricity that they have to be replaced. Amorphous cells are immune to these effects—a fortunate accident that was not foreseen when they were developed—and they should have a lifetime of around twenty years. The amorphous cells are not here yet; moreover, there remains the problem of electricity storage, which will be discussed shortly. The amorphous cells described above should have an efficiency of about 25 percent.

One other device under development is a "cascading solar cell." This is a group of solar cells combined into one; each cell in the group is designed to respond to a different frequency of light, so less energy of sunlight is lost. The total efficiency of the overall cell combination should be over 30 percent.

What happens to the solar energy a cell does not use? Most of it is given off by the cell as heat. For example, a cell may convert 20 percent of the sunlight shining on it into electricity, 70 percent of that sunlight into heat, and reflect the remaining 10 percent back at the sky. Ingenious plans have been devised whereby the heat generated by the cell (the 70 percent in the above example) is put to use. The University of Delaware built an experimental house called Solar One in 1973 that uses electricity from solar cells to run appliances, and heat from the cells for space heating. This raises the efficiency of the cells, since more of the sun's light is put to use; however, the cells are naturally not as effective at collecting heat as the solar collectors described in this book.

A problem that still afflicts solar cells in home application is the lack of a good way to store the electricity they generate. The available batteries and other devices suggested for this purpose simply will not do the job. Nothing on the market will satisfactorily store electricity generated during sunny hours so it is available when the sun is not shining. This is in marked contrast to the solar energy systems described earlier in this book, which have solved the problem of heat storage for times when the sun is not available. This may change in the future, just as the cost of electricity generated by solar cells can be expected to keep dropping. A breakthrough could be just around the corner; if and

164

when it appears, arrays of solar cells will sprout on rooftops all over the land, and our energy problems will be over.

For utilities themselves, storage is not so great a problem, since they already have extensive hardware to store electrical energy. Utilities store energy now so they can use their generators more efficiently when demand is low and have the extra electricity available when demand rises. Since they have the technology available, utilities could adapt it to solar cells, generating as much electricity as possible during sunlight hours and storing it for later use. They could also use solar cell arrays to generate extra electricity to meet extra high demand. This new attractiveness of solar cells to electric power companies presumably explains why we no longer see advertisements proclaiming that solar energy will only be practical *far* in the future.

Even in the 1960s, solar cells were acceptable for space applications, since they were cheaper and more efficient than any of the alternatives. At their present level of development, solar cells are widely used in such special applications as providing power for instrumented buoys floating far from land, and for research stations in the Antarctic. Even if they never reach the point where every home uses them to achieve complete energy independence, solar cells are already making major contributions. They now provide steady and dependable electricity for special uses in isolated places, thereby enabling us to do work that would otherwise be impossible.

# SOLAR ENERGY: LEGAL AND POLITICAL ASPECTS

A common question regarding solar energy is "What happens if I buy solar energy equipment, then someone builds something next door that casts shade on my collectors?" This chapter will consider other legal matters related to solar energy, but the above question is the central issue. There is no simple answer, but it's not because such an answer is unavailable. It's because for years courts and state legislatures of this country have ignored sun rights. Though there are not yet any laws specifically protecting solar collectors' access to sunlight, there are laws and regulations that affect solar energy systems, positively and negatively. The laws vary considerably from state to state, and the application of laws to solar energy is recent and in a state of flux, so you should consult a lawyer before buying a solar energy system. This was recommended earlier, as part of protecting yourself against fraud or inadequate consumer protection. Your lawyer should look into the legal status of solar energy in your state and city, and tell you whether you might encounter problems. If, by the time this book appears on the stands, your state has adopted one of the model bills that have been drawn up by various organizations to protect owners of solarized homes, you can probably avoid hiring a lawyer. Nonetheless, there is an incredible tangle of ramifications and precedents any time laws and courts are involved. Even a bill passed by a state legislature

166

can be called unconstitutional by that state's courts, or by federal courts, or there may be exceptions under the law that affect you negatively.

American law is essentially derived from the ancient body of tradition and law known as the English Common Law. Not all of the Common Law was adopted in America, and one part of it that was ignored was the Doctrine of Ancient Lights. This doctrine essentially says that if a house has received good light from outside for a long period of time, then that light cannot be taken away, or blocked—it has become a right of the homeowner. The length of time, under current English law, is twenty-seven years. The test for adequacy of light is that, in at least half a room, an average adult should be able to read without requiring artificial light. In modern times this test has been replaced with actual measurements, with the requirement now being that light must be at least one foot-candle illumination power on top of a thirty-three-inch-high desk in at least half a room. Naturally, this ancient law was not devised to protect solar collectors, and from the solar energy point of view, this is its drawback. The law does not require that direct sunlight be unblocked, but only that the remaining light be enough to read by. This would not be adequate for a solarized house. But if the Doctrine of Ancient Lights *were* part of American law, we would at least have some legal principle to build on. As it is, we have none. American courts have explicitly declared that no right to direct sunlight exists in this country. Does that leave the owner of a solarized home out in the cold? Perhaps not.

There is, as mentioned above, the possibility that your state legislature is working on some sort of sunlight protection bill. This is one way of making the right to sunlight a part of American law. Models for such bills are available, and they have in common a goal of protecting sunlight in a clear, unambiguous way. These bills will have to face a kind of inertia caused by the long American history of refusing to grant sun rights. There is a resistance in legislatures, which are reluctant to pass such bills, and resistance in courts, which are reluctant to find them constitutional once passed. There have even been examples of colonial court rulings,

167

based on the Doctrine of Ancient Lights, being overturned by postcolonial courts. The model bills try to avoid this pitfall by being careful about everything that could give a court an excuse to overturn them. Some even go so far as to call themselves "shade control" bills, rather than solar rights bills. Whether this will be acceptable to a suspicious and reluctant court system will be clear only after a few state legislatures have passed sun rights bills and the new laws have been challenged in courts.

At least in the case of roof-mounted collectors, there should be no shade problem from other buildings in residential areas. Problems would probably come primarily from trees or other shrubbery.

In the absence of a solar rights law, there are still other things that may protect a homeowner's access to sunlight. Zoning, land use plans, building codes, and a different sort of regulation, easements and covenants, are all potentially important for solar energy users.

Zoning and land use planning are somewhat related. A community or a state will often adopt a plan that tries to control how its land is used. This can be quite detailed, specifying what may be done or not done in a certain area, often trying to limit the use of natural resources so they won't run out. To enforce a land use plan in urban areas, zoning may be used. Zoning is practically universal in American cities and towns, including those not covered by a land use plan. In zoning, sections of a city are designated in various classifications; in a given classification, only certain types of buildings may be erected (for example, single-family dwellings). More importantly from the solar energy point of view, those buildings must meet certain specifications. In the case of single-family dwellings, zoning regulations will specify structural details, such as maximum height, minimum distance from the sidewalk and from a neighboring lot, and minimum performance by the heating system. Recent times have seen energy-related requirements added, such as minimum insulation or maximum heat loss.

Zoning tries to assure a certain minimum "quality of life" for residential neighborhoods. (This is the only type of zoning that

168

concern us in this book.) The disadvantage of zoning is that it causes uniformity and rigidity. In the case of a solar energy system, this can be an insurmountable barrier. For example, a limit on height could be interpreted to forbid solar collectors being added to a roof, if the total resulting height would exceed the maximum allowed. On the other hand, a city can decide that an addition such as a collector would not be counted in a building's height. Similarly, a new house with a solar collector would normally have a smaller, less complex furnace than another house, since the heating load on the furnace would not be as great as in a conventional house. But will zoning regulations permit this? As currently written and applied, they may not. Even the addition of a solar energy system may be forbidden, because its extra weight on a roof or the piping required may violate zoning regulations.

Here we move into the area of building codes and related permits, which present much the same problem. Here you may at least get an opinion on the permissibility of your proposed solar energy system by contacting a local building inspector. He has the responsibility to issue permits and decide whether a building or proposed building meets city codes. Some details of zoning regulations are harder to pin down; there is no one with the job of "zoning inspector," and the question of zoning violations often ends up in court.

On the positive side, zoning and building codes in your community may help solar energy systems rather than hinder them. Some cities have considered the idea of slipping the Ancient Lights Doctrine into their zoning regulations. This may or may not stand up in court. Any such regulation can be seen as limiting the rights of your neighbor to use his land as he wishes, and that would be unconstitutional. That was an argument against zoning when it first came into use in America early this century, and any new zoning concept must be handled with care so it is not seen as stepping on private property rights. Courts have said new zoning is good if some sort of land use plan exists, and the zoning is in line with it. This is a hopeful sign, since energy conservation, and hence the encouragement of solar energy systems, is increasingly a part of land use planning.

If a zoning law is passed that guarantees your access to direct sunlight, that law could limit what more than one of your neighbors can do on his land. This is the underlying constitutional problem, and cunning legal minds are at work on model zoning codes that will have this limiting effect without seeming to do so. Even if they succeed and the courts accept the result, two problems can arise.

First, the zoning code may be written in such a way that only some solar energy systems are protected. The system that would be best for you may not be one of them. Similarly, a zoning law may be written well from a legal view, but it does little good for the homeowner who wishes to solarize if it is technically inadequate and does not allow the protection from shade his collectors need. The second problem is perhaps more frightening: Even if the zoning is everything you could want, it may not be permanent. Changing conditions and urban growth can bring a change in the zoning classifications of a neighborhood, or even of the parcel of land adjacent to yours. In such cases, zoning laws will not protect your solar energy system.

If you cannot count on zoning laws or land use plans or building codes for much protection, and may even have much to fear from them, is the situation hopeless? Not necessarily. There are other legal avenues or remedies. Some are available now, and others may be available after courts have been forced to make more solar-rights-oriented decisions.

Covenants have become almost universal in newer residential neighborhoods. Covenants were mentioned in Chapter 11. Covenants are somewhat similar to provisions in zoning codes, though they tend to be more extensive and restrictive and apply to a particular subdivision. Covenants are a contractual agreement with the force of law. Like zoning codes, covenants impose limitations and minimum conditions of building size and architecture in a subdivision and often prescribe just what sort of fence a homeowner may erect. As with zoning codes, restrictions written into covenants may make solar energy systems illegal, even if there were no such intention to begin with. The homeowner cannot ignore covenants, just because they are not ordinances

170

enacted by the city council: If a person violates a covenant, his neighbors can take him to court, which will enforce the covenant as if it were law. Indeed, since a covenant is a contractual obligation that goes with the land (you submit to the obligation when you buy the land), it is as good as law.

Covenants can be friends instead of foes. In many cases, covenants are general, outlining requirements rather than stating them in narrow terms. The precise application of covenants is then left to a committee, which has the responsibility of approving or rejecting proposed building changes. This gives the committee leeway, and if the committee can be convinced of the desirability of solar energy systems in a subdivision, it will look kindly on plans to solarize houses. Developers are beginning to realize that solar energy in a subdivision can make the development more attractive to would-be home buyers. Interest is growing in solar covenants, covenants designed to encourage solar energy on houses, or at least covenants that do not stand in the way of solar energy. The most important feature of such covenants is a guarantee of direct sunlight—a restriction on the casting of shade into neighbors' yards. Similar covenants that attempt to guarantee light and air in more general terms have been upheld by courts, so the outlook here is hopeful. As with zoning, retrofitting is more likely to run into problems than building or buying a new house, since covenants or zoning classifications written years ago probably prohibit solar energy systems and do not protect solarized homes from loss of sunlight.

There is another legal avenue whereby the owner of a solarized house can protect his access to sunlight. In some ways this may be the best approach. This is a solar *easement*, an agreement under which a property owner relinquishes some rights he would normally enjoy on his own property. For this he may be paid, or he may give it away free. For example, a homeowner may allow a neighbor to build a driveway that covers part of his property. In practice this sort of agreement is usually made by verbal agreement, and no money changes hands. This avoids the tangle of lawyers and contracts and saves everyone money, but a verbal contract does not protect the owner of the driveway if a new

171

owner, less inclined to be a good neighbor, moves in next door. An easement clearly and specifically written out and signed by all involved may seem an unnecessary amount of work, but it can prevent serious legal trouble later. Normally, an easement becomes attached to the *property* involved (in this case, the owner's land), and not the person who initially obtained the easement. Future owners of the house can be sure they will have the same rights or benefits granted by the easement to the first owner.

Since easements are separate from zoning and covenants (although they must not violate them), sun rights acquired through an easement are free of the disadvantages discussed above for zoning and covenants. Easements have been around a long time, and are completely accepted by courts as a major legal principle. A properly written easement will not be thrown out by the courts. (There are tricky cases in which old easements have been declared invalid due to changes with the passage of time, but this should not be a problem with solar easements.) The possible drawback is the human factor. To guarantee your sunlight with an easement, you will probably have to persuade more than one neighbor to give you the right to the sunlight passing over his yard. The sunlight you need during the middle of winter, when the sun is lowest in the south, probably passes over a few yards south of your house. If you're thinking of solarizing, start being nice right now to your southerly neighbors! If you decide to pursue the easement idea, let your lawyer handle it. If he is vague on the subject of the solar easement, which is a new concept, you might refer him to the book listed at the end of this chapter.

One curious aspect of any kind of easement can be both an advantage and a disadvantage. When you obtain an easement from your neighbor (for instance, when he relinquishes the right to plant trees on his own property that will shade your house), the law considers your property as having gained value and your neighbor's as having lost it. Your neighbor has given up some control over his own property, and control gives land a good part of its value. While the easement increases the attractiveness of your property in case of resale, something any homeowner must keep in mind, it also increases its value from the point of view of the county tax assessor! It is possible the easement that works to your advantage can actually increase your property taxes as well. The bright spot in this picture is that your state legislature may be among those considering exempting solar easements from this sort of tax treatment. As you may have concluded, a lawyer is unfortunately indispensable in such matters.

There is another legal tradition that some experts suggest states or cities might use to protect homeowners' sun rights without upsetting the courts. This is the public nuisance law, under which all sorts of unrelated things have been declared and forbidden as public nuisances. Everything from prostitutes to pigeons to practicing law without a license has been declared a public nuisance at some time in some city. All sorts of environmental problems, such as excessive air pollution or wasting of natural resources, have fallen under this ancient legal doctrine. Solar energy advocates argue that cities should not hesitate to use public nuisance laws to forbid shade on solar collectors. There will be legal quibbling from opponents of this idea, and the courts, with their historical resistance to sun rights, may object to the whole idea. The outcome remains to be seen.

Even if there is no law or zoning in your city which protects your access to sunlight, and even if there is no covenant for your neighborhood or easement for your own parcel of land that provides that protection, you still have another way to protect your solar collectors' operation. Just as a city may declare something a public nuisance, so may a citizen bring suit against a "private nuisance." In the past, those trying to protect themselves against loss of light and air through private nuisance court suits have lost. One reason is that the law requires that the objectionable thing or action be a nuisance to a typical person in the community, rather than to one who is abnormally sensitive. The owner of a solar energy system has been considered significantly more sensitive to the loss of sunlight than the ordinary homeowner. In other cases, courts have decided against the bringer of the private nuisance suit in light and air cases, simply because courts don't like to guarantee access to direct sunlight. Such private nuisance suits have nonetheless continued, and they may certainly be expected to increase in the future, due to the increase in solar energy installations. Apart from the matter of solar energy, the public is becoming more assertive of its desire for light and air, more insistent that free access to light and air is a *right*. Sooner or later, the courts will have to wake up and join the rest of us in the Twentieth Century!

There is a trend apparent in the United States that bears a close watch, for it may affect solar energy. It is the use of public nuisance laws to prevent new architecture or changes to existing buildings that may be considered aesthetically displeasing. This seems a good idea, but the fly in the ointment is the definition of "aesthetic." We could see solar energy systems being declared aesthetically unacceptable. So far, however, this is only a possibility; it has not started happening in the United States.

It has been suggested that cities or states might use the ancient law of "eminent domain" to guarantee solar rights for homeowners. As with public nuisance law, this is an attempt to avoid major new concepts, such as solar zoning or solar covenants, which courts might declare unconstitutional. Eminent domain asserts a state or city's right to hold public need over private rights. Courts have long allowed cities and states to condemn property if the public's need for the action is great and overriding. Private property owners cannot block highways or electric power lines, though the citizen must be compensated fairly for what has been taken from him. The argument in a condemnation case usually revolves around the public's need (which also covers actions by companies such as utilities who serve the public directly), and what constitutes fair compensation. But the principle of eminent domain is well established. If eminent domain is used to try to obtain solar access rights, then we can expect those who lose control over their private property (those who are prevented from erecting on their own property anything that would shade another's solar collectors) will argue in court that the overriding need is that of a small, select group, *not* the public. If they can convince a court that the condemnation of their property is in a private, rather than public interest, then courts will probably decide in their favor, and against solar rights. Eminent domain is a tricky way to try to guarantee solar rights. It might not be an advisable route for a city or state to attempt.

There is another problem with condemnation. As mentioned above, those whose lands or property rights are taken away are entitled to fair compensation for their loss. Rather than have all taxpayers assume the burden of paying this compensation, the cost is often divided among those who benefit most directly from the use of eminent domain. In the case of eminent domain used to guarantee solar rights, it could be decided by a court, or by the authority exercising the right of eminent domain, that only the owners of solarized houses pay the cost. Whatever fair compensation is decided for those who lose some control over their land will be paid by people who live in solarized houses, and people who retrofit existing houses with solar energy systems. Depending on the amount of compensation and the size of the city, the amount paid by an individual homeowner could be steep.

Here are some legal odds and ends relating to solar rights.

If you live in an apartment building or condominium, someone might want to build or contract for a large solar energy system to take care of everyone at once, thereby cutting the cost to each individual. This is not a bad idea, but there is a possible legal entanglement. Such a "shared system" could be considered by your state's public utilities commission as coming under their jurisdiction; this has happened with similar installations. If this *were* to happen, life would suddenly become more complicated for you and your partners in the enterprise. You would then assume all the legal and economic responsibilities, requirements, paperwork, etc. of a public utility corporation. This must be weighed against the economic benefits of a shared system. If you're lucky, the public utilities commission in your state will let such a shared system operate without interference.

Utilities have a variety of rate structures, for a variety of reasons, which they apply to different customers. Some utilities have tried to hit back at solar energy systems, which they seem to view as their enemy, by requesting high rates for solarized houses. So far no utility has been granted these higher rates, but if one were, solar energy would lose some of its attractiveness. When you used the table in Chapter 10 to calculate the payback period, you assumed that if a solar energy system could take, say, 50 percent of your heating load, then that would cut your heating bills by about 50 percent. This would not be the case if your utility company raised your heating bill because you had solarized your home. You might only save 15 to 20 percent on your heating bills. The payback period would then be much longer, and you would be less inclined to buy a solar energy system. Why the electric or gas utility companies would wish to do this, aside from their weak argument that solar energy systems could increase the peak-load they must be prepared for, is a subject for another book.

Utility companies already have what are called "promotional rates." These are rate structures whereby larger users are actually charged less per kilowatt-hour or per hundred cubic feet of natural gas than smaller users. The reasoning behind this is to draw industry to the community. Since industry uses more energy than a residence, lower rates make the community attractive to companies seeking new locations. But this also means the homeowner who uses less energy pays the most per unit for it. The owner of a solarized home is thus penalized, in a manner of speaking, for his good citizenship. As with the punitive rates for solarized homes mentioned above, promotional rates now in effect mean savings on fuel bills for solarized houses would not be as great as they should be: You may use 50 percent less fuel, but you will really pay only 40 percent less, because you will pay more per unit of energy. (This is only an example. You must contact your utility company to find out what their promotional rates mean in your case.) The concept of promotional rates has been challenged in court by various citizens' groups with practically no success. At least the public is aware of the existence of these promotional rates and is demonstrating anger at their use. Perhaps public outcries will bring some reform soon.

Some utility companies have shown a laudable public spirit, especially from the solar energy view, by petitioning public utilities commissions to allow them to institute "lifeline rates."

These are special low rates for users of very little energy. The rates are an attempt to make matters easier for the poor and the elderly, who have suffered most of all from recent dramatic increases in fuel costs. Lifeline rates are not intended as an aid to solar energy systems, but they would in fact be a boon to owners of solarized homes, who would fall into the low-use category. Their savings on fuel bills would thus be greater than they might otherwise expect. This sounds almost too good to be true, and it is. Lifeline rate applications have been rejected by courts on the basis of the equal protection clause of the Constitution. (Why the same clause does not apply to promotional rates as well is a mystery.) It may take some time for the public to educate the courts on the issue of lifeline rates. A large part of the problem probably lies in the fact that judges are neither poor nor on a fixed income.

Chapter 10 mentioned that a solarized house raises special house insurance problems. A particular problem in this area is liability for injuries caused by the system. It may seem a bit far-fetched at first, but a roof-mounted collector could possibly cause injuries by reflecting sunlight. The glare in the eyes of a motorist or a pedestrian could conceivably cause an accident. (Pilots have reported being able to see the glare from solar collectors on the ground from thousands of feet in the sky.) A leak of toxic materials from a collector, or glass falling from a broken collector on a roof, could also cause serious injury. Difficulty could arise from a ground-based collector, which could, for example, injure a child who broke its glass. As stated in Chapter 10, this type of accident should be covered by a homeowner's existing liability insurance. But because this situation is still new and unusual, such an injury might result in a court case. This is especially true in the matter of glare from a collector, which is particularly novel. Even if the worst happens and a court finds against the homeowner, there is at least one opinion that the city or state that permitted such collectors to be installed would be held liable by courts. This situation is too unlikely to worry about; the worst that might be required of the homeowner by a nervous insurance company is somewhat higher premiums.

There is another complication. Certain injuries caused by a solar energy system might be due to an inadequacy in the system's construction, a defect in its design, manufacture, or installation. Courts will tend to hold the manufacturer liable for any settlement costs, under a wide range of circumstances. By selling a product, the manufacturer assumes a responsibility for the product being up to accepted standards of quality and safety. But the protection courts give the consumer usually extends only to questions of personal safety, although this apparently includes damage to a house that could endanger its inhabitants. Courts will not automatically offer you protection if a solar system performs inadequately but there is no question of safety involved. If your argument with a manufacturer is that the solar energy equipment does not deliver as much heat as you had expected, you will have a case only if an actual contract or warranty has been violated. This is a matter covered in Chapter 11.

### Additional Reading

Kraemer, Sandy F. *Solar law*. Colorado Springs, Colo.: Shepards Inc., 1978. Extensive coverage of legal aspects of solar energy, with copious references to legal literature. Not of great use to the ordinary consumer, but essential if you want to go into the matter deeply. A high point of the book is its carefully drawn model bills and ordinances, covenants and zoning regulations, easements, etc. Political activists advocating solar energy should have these at hand.

# EPILOGUE

For some time, we've all heard two extreme opinions about solar energy: (1) It isn't practical now, and we must look to coal, nuclear power, etc. to solve our energy problems; or (2) solar energy must be installed quickly in every house to save us from an energy disaster.

By now the reader has probably realized that the truth resides between these extremes. Solar energy is practical now—but not for every house and in all parts of the country. It can save the homeowner money in the long run—but it won't make most homeowners completely energy independent. Financing is available and laws are changing—but there are still problems.

This book has tried to present a balanced picture of the promises and problems of solar energy. The consumer must approach solar energy in a clear-eyed, level-headed way. But if he does so and decides that he should solarize his home, with competent, professional help, he will do more than just save money and insulate himself from the worst effects of the continuing energy crisis. He will have contributed significantly not only to his family's safety and welfare, but to the safety and welfare of his country as well. And he will have become part of a growing group of citizens who are laying a foundation of prosperity for their descendents.

# APPENDIX

## READING LIST

Here are books also mentioned at the end of various chapters. Where appropriate, there is a short and general review of the book; more details can be found where the book was first listed. The chapter number where the book was originally noted is provided in parentheses.

*General Books*

Anderson, Bruce. *The Solar Home Book*. Harrisville, N.H.: Cheshire Books, 1976. Borderline between general book and specialized book. Covers the field well, but best suited to those who want to experiment or build the whole thing themselves. (Chapters 6, 11)

Clark, Wilson. *Energy for Survival*. New York: Doubleday, 1975. Almost everything known about almost every energy source ever suggested by anyone. A remarkable and exceedingly thick book, hampered somewhat by the author's apparent lack of a technical background. (Chapter 1)

Commoner, Barry. *The Poverty of Power*. New York: Bantam, 1977. Covers ground similar to that covered by Hayes (below), though the emphasis is more sociological than environmental. Presents evidence that we are not running out of oil within the

United States, but that energy companies have stopped looking for it here, preferring the lower costs and higher profits of drilling for foreign oil. (Chapter 1)

Daniels, Farrington. *Direct Use of the Sun's Energy.* New York: Ballantine Books, 1975. The bible of the solar energy movement. In spite of its 1975 publication date, the text has not been updated since the mid-1960s; consequently, it is now somewhat outdated.

Foster, William M. *Homeowner's Guide to Solar Heating and Cooling.* Blue Ridge Summit, Pa.: Tab Books, 1976. Good overall view of the subject, though the chapters are in curious order. (Chapters 10, 11)

Halacy, Jr., D.S. *Earth, Water, Wind and Sun: Our Energy Alternatives.* New York: Harper and Row, 1977. Similar to *Energy for Survival* (above) but less massive. Halacy seems to have a better technical grounding than Clark. (Chapter 1)

Hayes, Denis. *Rays of Hope.* New York: W. W. Norton & Co., 1977. Hayes is a well-known environmental activist, and his biases show. An interesting survey of the uses of energy in the world throughout history. (Chapter 1)

Holdren, John and Herrera, Philip. *Energy.* San Francisco: Sierra Club, 1971. The socioeconomics of energy, the urgency of change, the problems with nuclear fission energy, and some alternatives. Not entirely objective, as you might guess from the publisher's name. (Chapter 1)

Lyons, Stephen, ed. *Sun! A Handbook for the Solar Decade.* San Francisco: Friends of the Earth, 1978. Contains interesting information and ideas, but the promise of strong bias implied by the title and publisher's name is amply fulfilled. (Chapter 1)

*Specialized Books*

Alves, Ronald and Milligan, Charles. *Living With Energy.* New York: Penguin Books, 1978. Interesting picture survey of energy-conserving and solar homes. (Chapter 12)

*ASHRAE Handbook of Fundamentals.* New York: The American Society of Heating, Refrigerating, and Air Conditioning

Engineers, 1974. Updated and republished occasionally. If Daniels's book (above) is the bible for solar energy, this is the concordance. (Chapter 6)

*Buying Solar.* By Federal Energy Administration. Useful consumer guide. (Chapter 10)

Campbell, Stu. *Build Your Own Solar Water Heater.* Charlotte, Vt.: Garden Way Publishing, 1978. (Chapter 3)

*Complete Do-It-Yourself Manual.* Pleasantville, N.Y.: Reader's Digest Association, 1974. How to repair your house from the foundation up. (Chapter 9)

*Consumer Reports Money-Saving Guide to Energy in the Home.* By Consumers Union. New York: Doubleday, 1978. Good workbook to help eliminate energy waste in your house. (Chapter 9)

Crowther, Richard L. *Sun, Wind, Earth.* Denver: Solar Group, 1977. Fairly technical book for architects; ask yours if he's read it yet. (Chapter 6)

Daniels, George. *Solar Homes and Sun Heating.* New York: Harper & Row, 1976. Do-it-yourself book. (Chapter 4)

Fuller, John G. *We Almost Lost Detroit.* New York: Reader's Digest Press, 1975. About a near-disaster at a nuclear power station, covered up at the time. (Chapter 1)

Hoyle, Fred. *Energy Or Extinction? The Case for Nuclear Energy.* Salem: N.H.: Heinemann Educational Books Limited, 1977. The pro-nuclear argument, presented by Sir Fred Hoyle, world-famous astrophysicist and cosmologist. As if to prove his opponents' point, Hoyle's book is very slim indeed. Will Hoyle's book be updated and reissued as a result of Three Mile Island?

*In the Bank Or Up the Chimney.* By U.S. Department of Housing and Urban Development. More energy saving tips. Also, instructions for installing insulation. (Chapter 9)

Kraemer, Sandy F. *Solar Law.* Colorado Springs, Colo.: Shepard's, Inc., 1978. Large book, just about the only one covering the whole topic that is easily available to the public. Legal jargon gets a bit thick in places. The lawyer you deal with should look at it. Also good for activists and legislators. (Chapter 14)

Kreider, Jan F. and Kreith, Frank. *Solar Heating and Cooling.* Washington, D.C.: Hemisphere Publishing Corporation, 1975. Technical treatment for architects, designers, and possibly experimenters. (Chapters 3, 6, 10)

Lucas, Ted. *How to Build a Solar Heater.* Pasadena, Calif.: Ward Ritchie Press, 1975. (Chapter 4)

Powers, Edward and Witt, James. *Traveling Weatherwise in the U.S.A.* New York: Dodd, Mead & Co., 1973. Amusing book for travelers, with detailed descriptions of weather and sun patterns in all regions of the United States. (Chapter 8)

Ruffner, James A. and Bair, Frank E. eds. *The Weather Almanac.* New York: Avon, 1979. Wealth of detail; stuffed with tables and maps. (Chapter 8)

Scortia, Thomas N. and Robinson, Frank M. *The Prometheus Crisis.* New York: Doubleday, 1975. Novel describing what would have happened if the "almost lost" in Fuller's title (above) had been "did lose." (Chapter 1)

Skurka, Norma and Naar, John. *Design for a Limited Planet.* New York: Ballantine Books, 1977. Similar to Alves and Milligan's book (above), with more text and fewer pictures. Oriented more toward design principles and their implementation than the appearance of the result. Emphasis on function rather than beauty.

Stein, Richard G. *Architecture and Energy.* New York: Anchor Books/Doubleday, 1978. For architects, but of more general interest than either Crowther's or Wright's books. (Chapter 6)

*Tips for Consumers Insulating Their Homes.* U.S. Government pamphlet. Free booklet on buying and installing insulation. (Chapter 9)

*Tips for Energy Savers.* By U.S. Department of Energy, 1978. Copious suggestions for saving energy. Free. (Chapter 9)

Wright, David. *Natural Solar Architecture: A Passive Primer.* New York: Van Nostrand, Reinhold Co., 1978. Written by an architect for architects. Similar to *Sun, Wind, Earth.* (Chapter 6)

# SOLAR EQUIPMENT MANUFACTURERS

The following list of manufacturers of solar energy products should provide the reader with many local or regional sources of information about specific products and prices. This is not a list of every manufacturer in the country, since such a list would require a book in itself. (Such complete lists are available; sources for them are given below.) This list is restricted to those companies that are in business now and were already in business at the start of 1977; the reason for using these criteria was discussed in Chapter 11.

The companies listed here are those carried on the regularly updated computerized data base maintained by the Solar Energy Research Institute (SERI) in Golden, Colorado. Inevitably, there are some solar energy manufacturers who have been in existence since before the beginning of 1977 but are not listed here. There are two reasons for this. First, there are a few companies which, for a variety of reasons, are simply not carried on SERI's data base; in some cases, they may simply not have wished to provide SERI with the requested information. Second, quite a few companies did not provide SERI with their founding date, and so there was no way for the computer to know whether they have been in business for long enough to qualify or not; they were therefore omitted.

Some of the companies listed below are not currently selling products or services to the general public; this is especially true of those which are subsidiaries of large, well-established corporations. Such companies currently derive most of their income either from government study contracts (primarily from the Department of Energy) or from selling their products to other companies, which in turn sell complete systems to the public. Nonetheless, they are still potential sources of product information and, as the solar energy market continues to expand, many of them will doubtless begin to sell directly to the public.

# Appendix

## Arizona

Arizona Engineering & Refrigeration, 635 West Commerce Avenue, Gilbert, AZ 85234

Cementitious Products, 3136 N. 28th Ave., Phoenix, AZ 85017

Ecotronics, Inc., 7745 E. Redfield Rd., Scottsdale, AZ 85260

Gila River Products, Inc., 6615 W. Boston St., Chandler, AZ 85224

Hansberger Refrigeration & Electric Company, 2450 8th St., Yuma, AZ 85364

Hughes-Calihan Corp., 4730 N. 16th Street, Phoenix, AZ 85016

Matrix, Inc., 537 S. 31st Street, Mesa, AZ 85204

Sebra Solar Energy, Era Plaza, 500 N. Tuscon Blvd., Tuscon, AZ 85716

Smith Pre-Cast, Inc. 2410 W. Broadway, Phoenix, AZ 85339

## California

Aero Power Systems, Inc., 2398 4th St., Berkeley, CA 94710

American Appliance Mfg. Corp., 2341 Michigan Ave., Santa Monica, CA 90404

American Sun Industries, 996 Lawrence Dr., Newbury Park, CA 91320

Arco Solar, Inc., 20554 Plummer St., Chatsworth, CA 91311

Beam Engineering, Inc., 732 N. Pastoria Ave., Sunnyvale, CA 94086

Budge-It Home Remodeling Inc., 2553 State St., San Diego, CA 92101

Burke Industries, Inc., 2250 S. 10th St., San Jose, CA 95112

California Measurements, 150 E. Montecito Ave., P.O. Box 594, Sierra Madre, CA 91024

Catel Manufacturing, Inc., 243 W. Maple Ave., Monrovia, CA 91016

Chronomite Labs, 21011 S. Figueroa, Carson, CA 90745

Clover Solar Corp., 600 E. Colorado St., Glendale, CA 91205

Colt Inc. of Southern California, 71590 San Jacinto Dr., Rancho Mirage, CA 92270

Com Pu Corp., 333 Fairchild Dr., Mountain View, CA 94043

Conserdyne Corp., 4437 San Fernando Rd., Glendale, CA 91204

Davis Instruments Corp., 642 143rd Ave., P.O. Box 3157, San Leandro, CA 94578

Diamond Patent Co., 429 S. Canal, South San Francisco, CA 94080

Elcam, Inc., Sunspot Div., 5330 Debbie Lane, Santa Barbara, CA 93111

Energy Systems, Inc., 4750 Alvarado Canyon Rd., San Diego, CA 92120

Fabco Sun-X, 809 E. 18th St., Los Angeles, CA 90021

Fafco, Inc., 235 Constitution Dr., Menlo Park, CA 94025

Farwest Corrosion Control Co., 17311 S. Main St., Gardena, CA 90248

Flo Control, Inc., 3210 Winona Ave., Burbank, CA 91510

General Atomic Co., 10955 John Jay Hopkins Dr., San Diego, CA 92138

General Sealants Corp., 15248 E. Proctor Ave., City of Industry, CA 91744

Grundfos Pumps Corp., 2555 Clovis Ave., Clovis, CA 93612

Global Marine Development, Inc., 4100 MacArthur Blvd., Newport Beach, CA 92600

Heliotrope General, 3733 Kenora Dr., Spring Valley, CA 92077

Hy-Cal Engineering, 12105 E. Los Nietos Rd., Santa Fe Springs, CA 90670

Imex Trading, 3315 Como Ln., San Jose, CA 95118

Kahl Scientific Instrument Corp., 733 W. Main St., El Cajon, CA 92022

Kedco, Inc., 9016 Aviation Blvd., Inglewood, CA 90301

# At Home With Solar Energy

Kessel Insolar System, 2135 Mono Way, Sonora, CA 95370
L. M. Dearing Assoc., Inc., 12324 Ventura Blvd., P.O. Box 144, Studio City, CA 91604
Lockheed Missiles & Space Co., Inc., 1111 Lockheed Way, Sunnyvale, CA 94088
M. C. Nottingham Co. of California, P.O. Box 7007, 890 S. Arroyo Parkway, Pasadena, CA 91109
Meteorology Research, Inc., 464 W. Woodbury Rd., Altadena, CA 91001
Micropump Corp., 1015 Shary Ct., Concord, CA 94518
Molectron Corp., 177 N. Wolf Rd., Sunnyvale, CA 94086
Monitor Labs, Inc., 10180 Scripps Ranch Blvd., San Diego, CA 92131
Ocean Shore Iron Works, 1660 Jerrold Ave., San Francisco, CA 94124
Omnium-G, 1815 Orangethorpe Park, Complex B, Anaheim, CA 92801
Optical Coating Lab, Inc., Energy Products Div., 2789 Giffen Ave., Santa Rosa, CA 95403
Optical Sciences Group, Inc., 24 Tiburon St., San Rafael, CA 94901
Owen Enterprises, 436 N. Fries Ave., Wilmington, CA 90744
Piper Hydro, Inc., 3031 E. Coronado, Anaheim, CA 92806
Premier Pump & Pool Products, Inc., 3347 San Fernando Rd., Los Angeles, CA 90065
Radco Products, Inc., 2877 Industrial Pkwy, Santa Maria, CA 93454
Rho Sigma, 1192 Valeria St., North Hollywood, CA 91605
Sencenbaugh Wind Electric, 2235 Old Middlefield Way, Mt. View, CA 94040
Sensor Technology, Inc., 21012 Lassen St., Chatsworth, CA 91311
Shaw Pump Co., 9660 E. Rush St., South El Monte, CA 91733
Silicon Material, Inc., 341 Moffett Blvd., Mountain View, CA 94043
Siltec Corp., 3717 Haven Ave., Menlo Park, CA 94025
Solarcoa, Inc., 2115 E. Spring St., Long Beach, CA 90806
Solergy, Inc., 70 Zoe St., San Francisco, CA 94107
Sollos, Inc., 2231 Carmelina Ave., Los Angeles, CA 90064
Spectrolab, Inc., 12500 Gladstone Ave., Sylmar, CA 91342
Sundu Co., 3319 Keys Ln., Anaheim, CA 92804
Sun of Man Solar Systems, Drawer W, Bethel Island, CA 94511
Swedlow, Inc., 12122 Western Ave., Garden Grove, CA 92645
Varian Assoc., 611 Hansen Way, Palo Alto, CA 94303
Western Energy, Inc., 454 Forest Ave., Palo Alto, CA 94302
Ying Manufacturing Corp., 1957 W. 144th St., Gardena, CA 90249

Colorado
Alternative Heating Systems, Inc., 3163 Walnut, Boulder, CO 80301
American Energy Alternatives, P.O. Box 905, Boulder, CO 80302
American Heliothermal Corp., 2625 S. Santa Fe. Dr., Denver, CO 80223
Eaton Metal Products Co., 4800 York St., Denver, CO 80216
Energy Dynamics Corp., 6062 E. 49th Ave., Commerce City, CO 80022
Federal Energy Corp., 5505 E. Evans Ave., Denver, CO 80222
Housewarming Development Corp., 959 Walnut, Boulder, CO 80306
Lof Bros. Solar Appliances, 1615 17th St., Denver, CO 80202
R-M Products, Inc., 5010 Cook St., Denver, CO 80216

# Appendix

Solar Energy Research Corp., 1224 Sherman Dr., Longmont, CO 80501
Solaron Corp., 720 S. Colorado Blvd., Denver, CO 80222
Solar Technology Corp., 2160 Clay St., Denver, CO 80211
Zia Assoc., Inc., 5590 Arapahoe, P.O. Box 1466 Boulder, CO 80302

### Connecticut

American Solar Heat Corp., 7 National Plc., Danbury, CT 06810
C & M Systems, Inc., P.O. Box 475, Old Saybrook, CT 06475
Falbel Energy Systems Corp., 472 Westover Rd., Greenwich, CT 06830
Hubbell, The Electric Heater Co., 45 Seymour St., Stratford, CT 06497
Inotech Corp., 2285 Reservoir Ave., Trumbull, CT 06611
Int'l Environment Corp. 133 Byram Shore Rd., Greenwich, CT 06830
Kem Assoc., 153 East St., New Haven, CT 06507
Lassy Tools, Inc., 96 Bohemia St., Plainville, CT 06062
Nuclear Technology Corp., P.O. Box 1, Rt. 85, Amston, CT 06231
Oriel Corp. of America, 15 Market St., Stamford, CT 06902
Resource Technology Corp., 151 John Downey Dr., New Britain, CT 06051
Seymour-Sheridan, Inc., 264 Seymour St., Stratford, CT 06497
Wormser Scientific Corp., 88 Foxwood Rd., Stamford, CT 06903

### Delaware

Chemax Corp., 211 River Rd., New Castle, DE 19720
E. I. Du Pont De Nemours & Co., Inc., Plastic Products & Resins Dept., 1007
Market St., Room D-13126, Wilmington, DE 19898

### District of Columbia

Business & Technology, Inc., 2800 Upton St. NW, Washington, DC 20008

### Florida

All Sunpower, Inc., 10400 SW 187th St., Miami, FL 33157
Aquasolar, Inc., 1234 Zacchini Ave., Sarasota, FL 33577
Automated Bldg. Components, Inc., 7525 NW 37th Ave., Miami, FL 33159
Aztec Solar Co., 2031 Dyan Way, Maitland, FL 32751
Beutels Solar Heating Co., 7161 NW 74th St., Miama, FL 33166
Capital Solar Heating, Inc., 376 NW 25th St., Miama, FL 33127
CBM Manufacturing, Inc., 621 NW 6th Ave., Ft. Lauderdale, FL 33311
Celotex Corp., P.O. Box 22602, Tampa, FL 33622
Chemical Processors, Inc., 2434 22nd St. N., St. Petersburg, FL 33733
Consumer Energy Corp., 4234 SW 75th Ave., Miami, FL 33155
CSI, Solar Systems Div., 12400 49th St., Clearwater, FL 33520
Deko Labs, 3860 SW Archer Rd., Gainesville, FL 32604
D. W. Browning Contracting Co., 475 Carswell Ave., Holly Hill, FL 32017
Electrasol Labs, Inc., 2326 Fieldingwood Rd., Maitland, FL 32751
FHP Manufacturing Corp., 610 SW 12th Ave., Pompano Beach, FL 33060
Flagala Corp., 9700 Highway 98, Panama City, FL 32401
Florida Solar Power, Inc., 1327 S. Monroe St., Box 5846, Tallahassee, FL 32301
Gulf Thermal Corp., 629 17th Ave. W., Bradenton, FL 33505
Horizon Enterprises, Inc., 1011 NW 6th St., P.O. Box V, Homestead, FL 33030

# At Home With Solar Energy

Kinetics Corp., 1121 Lewis Ave., Sarasota, FL 33577
Lab Sciences, 604 Park Dr., University Pk., Boca Raton, FL 33431
Largo Solar Systems, Inc., 991 SW 40th Ave., Plantation, FL 33317
Rox International, Inc., Presidential Suite D, 2604 Hidden Lake Dr., Sarasota, FL 33577
Solar Energy Products, Inc., 1208 NW 8th Ave., Gainesville, FL 32601
Sun Harvesters, Inc., 211 NE 5th St., Ocala, FL 32670
W. R. Robbins & Son Roofing Co., 1401 NW 20th St., Miami, FL 33142

Georgia
Atlanta Stove Works, Inc., 112 Krog NE, P.O. Box 5254, Atlanta, GA 30307
Independent Living, Inc., 5965 Peachtree Corner E., Suite A-4, Norcross, GA 30071
Industrial Boiler Co., 221 Law Street, Thomasville, GA 31792
MND, Inc., 1207 Reeder Circle, Atlanta, GA 30306

Hawaii
Precision Industries, Ltd., 928 Kaamahu Pl., Honolulu, HI 96817
Solaray Corp., 2414 Makiki Heights Dr., Honolulu, HI 96322

Idaho
MNK Enterprises, Inc., 10 S. 1st E., P.O. Box 87, Bancroft, ID 83217

Illinois
Airtex Corp., 2900 N. Western Ave., Chicago, IL 60618
Barber-Colman Co., 1300 Rock St., Rockford, IL 61101
Desoto, Inc., 1700 S. Mount Prospect Rd., Des Plaines, IL 60018
Heat Exchangers, Inc., Koldwave Div., 8100 N. Monticello, Skokie, IL 60076
Hi-Tech, Inc., 3204 16th St., Zion, IL 60099
Insta-Foam Products, Inc., 2050 N. Broadway, Joliet, IL 60435
Kewanee Boiler Corp., 101 Franklin St., Kewanee, IL 61443
March Manufacturing Co., Inc., 1819 Pickwick Ave., Glenview, IL 60025
Metraflex Co., 2323 W. Hubbard St., Chicago, IL 60612
Mohawk Steel Corp., 520 N. Michigan, Chicago, IL 60611
Pak-Tronics, Inc., 4044 N. Rockwell Ave., Chicago, IL 60618
Shelley Radiant Ceiling Co., 456 W. Frontage Rd., Northfield, IL 60093
Sun Trac Corporation, 540 Zenith Dr., Glenview, IL 60025

Indiana
A/C Fabricating Corp., 64598 U.S. 33 E., P.O. Box 774, Goshen, IN 46526
Durakool, Inc., 1010 N. Main St., Elkhart, IN 46514
Elkhart Products Corp., 1255 Oak St., P.O. Box 1008, Elkhart, IN 46515
Refrigeration Systems Co., Inc., 4241 Hogue Rd., Evansville, IN 47712
Thrush Products, Inc., P.O. Box 228, Peru, IN 46970

Iowa
Amana Refrigeration, Inc., Main St., Amana, IA 52204
Impac Corp., 312 Blondeau, Keokuk, IA 52623
Lennox Industries, 200 S. 12th Ave., Box 250, Marshalltown, IA 50158

# Appendix

## Kansas
Hydro-Flex Corp., 2101 NW Brickyard Rd., Topeka, KS 66618
Peabody Gordon-Piatt, Strother Field Ind. Comp., Winfield, KS 67156

## Kentucky
Louisville Tin & Stove Co., 737 S. 13th St., Louisville, KY 40201

## Maine
Dover Stove Co., Main St., Sangerville, ME 04479
Dumont Industries, Main St., Monmouth, ME 04259
Shape, Symmetry & Sun, Inc., Biddeford Industrial Park, Biddeford, ME 04005
The Merry Music Box, 20 McKown St., Boothbay Harbor, ME 04538

## Maryland
AAI Corp., P.O. Box 6767, Baltimore, MD 21204
Belfort Instrument Co., 1600 S. Clinton St., Baltimore, MD 21224
Payne, Inc., 1933 Lincoln Dr., Annapolis, MD 21401
Powrmatic, Inc., 2906 Baltimore Blvd., Finksburg, MD 21048
Solarex Corp., 1335 Piccard Dr., Rockville, MD 20850
Thomason Solar Homes, Inc., 609 Cedar Ave., Oxon Hill, Fort Washington, MD 20022

## Massachusetts
Andover Controls, P.O. Box 34, Shawsheen Village Station, Andover, MA 01810
Arthur D. Little, Inc., 25 Acorn Park, Cambridge, MA 02140
Chase-Walton Elastomers, Inc., 29 Apsley St., Hudson, MA 01749
Crystal Systems, Inc., Shetland Ind. Park, 35 Congress St., Salem, MA 01970
Dampney Co., 85 Paris St., Everett, MA 02149
Daystar Corp., 90 Cambridge St., Burlington, MA 01803
Dennison Mfg. Co., 300 Howard St., Framingham, MA 01701
Devcon Corp., Endicott St., Danvers, MA 01923
Dixon Energy Systems, Inc., 47 East St., Hadley, MA 01035
Diy-Sol, Inc., 29 Highgate Rd., Marlboro, MA 01752
Ecos, Inc., Damon Mill Square, Concord, MA 01742
Elbart Manuf. Co., 127 Main St., Millbury, MA 01527
Foster-Miller Assoc., 350 Second Ave., Waltham, MA 02154
Lion Precision Corp., 60 Bridge St., Newton, MA 02158
M. C. Stewart Co., Crosby Rd., Ashburnham, MA 01430
Megatech Corp., 29 Cook St., Billerica, MA 01821
Mobil Tyco Solar Energy Corp., 16 Hickory Dr., Waltham, MA 02154
Mohawk Industries, Inc., 173 Howland Ave., Adams, MA 01220
Pinson Energy Corp., Box 7, Marstons Mills, MA 02648
Raytheon Co., 141 Spring St., Lexington, MA 02173
Semicon, Inc., 10 North Ave., Burlington, MA 01803
Sheffield Plastics, Inc., Salisbury Rd., Sheffield, MA 01257
Solar Power Corp., 20 Cabot Rd., Woburn, MA 01801
Spire Corp., Patriots Park, Bedford, MA 01730
Sun Systems, Inc., P.O. Box 347, Milton, MA 02186

189

# At Home With Solar Energy

## Michigan
Addison Products Co., Solar Div., 215 N. Talbot St., Addison MI, 49220
Attwood Corp., 1016 N. Monroe, Lowell, MI 49331
Champion Home Builders Co., Solar Div., 5573 E. North, Dryden, MI 48428
Dow Corning, 2200 W. Salzburg Rd., Midland, MI 48640
Electric Motor Repair and Service, Country Rd. 645, Lake Leelanau, MI 49653
Environmental Energies, Inc., Front St., Copemish, MI 49625
Ford Motor Co., Glass Div., 300 Renaissance Ctr., P.O. Box 43343, Detroit, MI 48243
Guardian Industries Corp., 43043 W. Nine Mile Rd., Northville, MI 48167
Heat Controller, Inc., 1900 Wellworth Ave., P.O. Box 1089, Jackson, MI 49203
Midwest Components, Inc., 1981 Port City Blvd., Muskegon, MI 49443
Mueller Brass Co., 1925 Lapeer, Port Huron, MI 48060
Polynesian Pools, 1145 S. Washington Ave., Holland, MI 49423
Ram Products, 1111 N. Centerville Rd., Sturgis, MI 49091
Refrigeration Research, Inc., Solar Research Div., 525 N. Fifth St., Brighton, MI 48116
Sensors, Inc., 3908 Varsity Dr., P.O. Box 1383, Ann Arbor, MI 48106
Solarator, Inc., 16231 W. 14 Mile Rd., Birmingham, MI 48009
Vinyl Fab Inc., 13550 Otterson Ct., Livonia, MI 48150

## Minnesota
Charmaster Products, Inc., 2307 Hwy 2 W., Grand Rapids, MN 55744
Ilse Engineering, Inc., 7177 Arrowhead Rd., Duluth, MN 55811
3 M Co., 3 M Ctr, Bldg. 223-2, St. Paul, MN 55101

## Missouri
Crimsco, Inc., 5001 E. 59th St., Kansas City, MO 64130
Longwood Furnace Corp., 4 Mi. E. on Hwy. 6, Gallatin, MO 64640
Monsanto Corp., 800 N. Lindbergh Blvd., St. Louis, MO 63166
Vactec, Inc., 2423 Northline Ind. Blvd., Maryland Heights, MO 63043

## Montana
Independent Power Developers, Box 1467, Noxon, MT 59853
Ryniker Steel Products Co., P.O. Box 1932, N.P. Industrial Site, Billings, MT 59103

## Nebraska
Dempster Industries, Inc., 711 S. 6th St., Beatrice, NE 68310
Lambda Instruments Corp., 4421 Superior St., Lincoln, NE 68504

## Nevada
Richdel, Inc., 1851 Oregon, P.O. Drawer A, Carson City, NV 89701

## New Hampshire
Hydraform Products Corp., Samspon Dr., Rochester, NH 03867
Kalwall Corp., Solar Components Div., 88 Pine St., Manchester, NH 03105
Natural Power, Inc., Francestown Turnpike, New Boston, NH 03070

190

# Appendix

## New Jersey

Airtemp, Woodbridge Ave., Edison, NJ 08817
Automatic Switch Co., 50-56 Hanover Rd., Florham Park, NJ 07932
Bailey Instruments, 515 Victor St., Saddle Brook, NJ 07662
Berry Solar Products, Woodbridge at Main, P.O. Box 327, Edison, NJ 08817
Burling Instrument Co., 16 River Rd., Chatham, NJ 07928
Calmac Manufacturing Corp., 150 S. Van Brunt St., Englewood, NJ 07631
Chemplast, Inc., 150 Dey Rd., Wayne, NJ 07470
Croton Chemical Co., 10 Harmich Rd., South Plainfield, NJ 07080
Cy/Ro Industries, Berdan Ave., Wayne, NJ 07470
Edwards Engineering Corp., 101 Alexander Ave., Pompton Plains, NJ 07444
Federal Boiler Co., Inc., 227 Fairfield Rd., Fairfield, NJ 07407
Gusmer Corp., One Gusmer Dr., Lakewood, NJ 08701
Heilemann Electric, 127 Mountainview Rd., Warren, NJ 07060
Multi-Research Corp., Solarad Div., Keyport, NJ 07735
New Jersey Aluminum Corp., 101 Jersey Ave., P.O. Box 73, North Brunswick, NJ 08902
Omnidata, Inc., 16 Springdale Rd., Cherry Hill, NJ 08003
Rife Hydraulic Engine Mfg. Co., Box 367, Millburn, NJ 07041
Science Assoc., Inc., Box 230, 230 Nassau St., Princeton, NJ 08540
Solar Energy Systems, Inc., One Olney Ave., Cherry Hill Industrial Ctr., Cherry Hill, NJ 08003
Solar Industries, Inc., Monmouth Airport Industrial Park, Farmingdale, NJ 07727

## New Mexico

Solar America, Inc., 2620 San Mateo, NE, Albuquerque, NM 87110
Solar Room Co., Box 1377, Taos, NM 87571
Zomeworks Corp., P.O. Box 712, Albuquerque, NM 87103

## New York

ABC Solar Systems, 329 Central Ave., Albany, NY 12206
Aldrich Roofing Co., 142 Cannon St., Poughkeepsie, NY 12601
American Acrylic Corp., 173 Marine St., Farmingdale, NY 11735
Bio-Energy Systems, Inc., Mountaindale Rd., Spring Glen, NY 12483
Custom Solar Heating Systems Co., P.O. Box 375, Albany, NY 12201
Ecosol Ltd., 2 W. 59th St., New York, NY 10019
Energy Designs, Inc., 1925 Curry Rd., Schenectedy, NY 12303
Flair Mfg. Corp., 600 Old Willetts Path, Hauppauge, NY 11787
Ford Products Corp., Ford Products Rd., Valley College, NY 10989
James Catalano & Sons, Inc., 301 Stagg St., Brooklyn, NY 11206
Kingston Industries Corp., 205 Lexington Ave., New York, NY 10016
Lomart Industries, 960 Alabama Ave., Brooklyn, NY 11207
Marathon Heater Co., Inc., Quayle Hollow Rd., Marathon, NY 13803
Mechanical Mirror Works, Inc., 661-663 Edgecombe Ave., New York, NY 10032
Northeastern Solar Energy Corp., 107 Northern Blvd., Great Neck, NY 11021
Pawling Rubber Corp., 157 Maple Blvd., Pawling, NY 12564

# At Home With Solar Energy

Phelps Dodge Industries, Inc., 300 Park Ave., New York, NY 10022
Robert Mitchell Solar Systems Design, Rd 3, Box 147, Selkirk, NY 12158
Rush Mfg. Corp., 381 Huguenot St., New Rochelle, NY 10801
Solar Sunstill, Inc., 15 Blueberry Ridge Rd., Srauker, NY 11733
Sturges Heat Recovery, Inc., P.O. Box 397, Stone Ridge, NY 12484
Sunray Solar Heat, Inc., 202 Classon Ave., Brooklyn, NY 11205

## North Carolina
Carolina Thermal Co., Iron Works Rd., Reidsville, NC 27320
Energy Applications, Inc., Lattionore Rd., Rutherfordton, NC 28139

## Ohio
Acme Boiler Co., 3718 Ridge Rd., Cleveland, OH 44144
Airloc, Inc., 337 Elm St., Struthers, OH 44471
Alcan Aluminum Corp., 100 Erie View Plaza, Cleveland, OH 44110
Bard Mfg. Co., 520 Evansport Rd., Bryan, OH 43506
Ferro Corp., 1 Erie View Plaza, Cleveland, OH 44114
Fiber Forms, Inc., 100 S. 22nd St., Newark, OH 43055
Fiber-Rite Products, 1328 Linda St., Cleveland, OH 44116
Fomo Products, Inc., 1090 N. Jacoby Rd., P.O. Box 4261, Akron, OH 44321
Glass-Lined Water Heater Co., 13000 Athens Ave., Cleveland, OH 44107
Heller-Aller Co., 900 Oakwood Ave., Napoleon, OH 43545
Inservco, Inc., 110 Commerce Dr., La Grange, OH 44050
Kuss Corp., 1331 Broad Ave., P.O. Box 886, Findlay, OH 45840
Mansfield Industries, Inc., 1776 Harrington Memorial Blvd., Mansfield, OH 44901
Mor-Flo Industries, Inc., 18450 S. Miles Rd., Cleveland, OH 44128
NRG Mfg., P.O. Box 53, Napoleon, OH 43545
Owens Corning Fiberglass Corp., Fiberglass Tower, Toledo, OH 43659
Owens-Illinois, Inc., 405 Madison Ave., Toledo, OH 43666
REM Industries, Simms Building, Dayton, OH 45402
Solar Energy Products Co., 121 Miller Rd., Avon Lake, OH 44012
Sunpower, Inc., 48 W. Union St., Athens, OH 45701
Turbonics, Inc., 11200 Madison Ave., Cleveland, OH 44102

## Oklahoma
American Wind Turbine, Inc., 1016 E. Airport Rd., Stillwater, OK 74074
Brown Mfg. Co., 13431 Broadway Extension, P.O. Box 14546, Oklahoma City, OK 73114
McKim Solar Energy Systems, Inc., 1142 E. 64th St., Tulsa, OK 74136
Professional Fiberglass Products, Inc., Ada Industrial Park, Box 1179, Ada, OK 74820

## Oregon
Fire-View, P.O. Box 370, Rogue River, OR 97537
Harris Thermal Products, Inc., 19830 SW 102nd St., Tualatin, OR 97062
Kastek Corp., 838 N. Watts, Portland, OR 97208
Leupold & Stevens, Inc., 600 NW Meadow Dr., Beaverton, OR 97005

# Appendix

## Pennsylvania
Atlas Vinyl Products, Free Heat Div., 7002 Beaverdam Rd., Levittown, PA 19057
Dumore Sales Co., 675 Rose St., Williamsport, PA 17701
Enviropane, Inc., 350 N. Marshall St., Lancaster, PA 17602
Foam Products, Inc., Gay St., York Haven, PA 17370
Peerless Heater Co., Boyertown, PA 19512
Pittsburgh Corning Corp., 800 Presque Isle Dr., Pittsburgh, PA 15239
PPG Industries, Inc., 1 Gateway Ctr., Pittsburgh, PA 15222
Practical Solar Heat, Inc., 2216 Montgomery St., Bethlehem, PA 18017
Ridgeway Steel Fabricators, Inc., Hydroheat Div. P.O. Box 382, Ridgeway, PA 15853
Rohm & Haas Co., Independence Mall W., Philadelphia, PA 19105
Sunwall, Inc., 113 Snowden, P.O. Box 9723 Pittsburgh, PA 15229

## Rhode Island
Amtrol, Inc., 1400 Division Rd., West Warwick, RI 02893
Elmwood Sensors, Inc., 1655 Elmwood Ave., Cranston, RI 02907
Eppley Lab, Inc., 12 Sheffield Ave., Newport, RI 02840
Independent Energy, Inc., P.O. Box 732, 42 Ladd St., E. Greenwich, RI 02818

## South Carolina
Ballard Concrete Co., P.O. Box 7175, Greenville, SC 29610

## South Dakota
Product Development Co., 3901 Red Rock Canyon Rd., Rapid City, SD 57701

## Tennessee
ASG Industries, Inc., 1400 Lincoln St., Kingsport, TN 37662
Brown Stove Works, Inc., 1422 Carolina Ave. NE, Cleveland, TN 37311
Dalen Products, Inc., 201 Sherlake Dr., Knoxville, TN 37922
Eastman Chemical Products, Inc., 200 S. Wilcox, Kingsport, TN 37662
Energy Converters, Inc., 2501 N. Orchard Knob Ave., Chattanooga, TN 37406
Memphis Pump & Mfg. Co., Inc., 4000 Winchester Rd., Memphis TN 38118
W. L. Jackson Mfg. Co., Inc., 1200-26 E. 40th St., P.O. Box 11168, Chattanooga, TN 37401

## Texas
Ace Solar Systems, Rt. 1, Box 50, Mission, TX 78572
American Permanent Ware Co., 729 3rd St., Box 26070, Dallas, TX 75226
American Solar King Corp., 6801 New McGregor Hwy., Waco, TX 76710
Automatic Power, Inc., 213 Hutcheson St., Houston, TX 77023
Butler Ventamatic Corp., P.O. Box 728, Mineral Wells, TX 76067
Cole Solar Systems, Inc., 440a E. St. Elmo Rd., Austin, TX 78745
Command-Aire Corp., 3221 Speight, Waco, TX 76710
Dodge Products, Inc., 57 Patti Lynn Ln., Houston, TX 77024
E-Systems, Inc., Energy Technology Ctr., P.O. Box 6118, Dallas, TX 75222
Jamak, Inc., 1401 N. Bowie Dr., Weatherford, TX 76086

## At Home With Solar Energy

Lectric Lites Co., 2504 W. Vickery Blvd., Fort Worth, TX 76102
Northrup, Inc., 302 Nichols Dr., Hutchins, TX 75141
Packless Industries, P.O. Box 8799, Waco, TX 76710
Pres Clancey & Assoc., 11031 Wye Dr., San Antonio, TX 78217
Solar Kinetics, Inc., 8120 Chancellor Row, Dallas, TX 75247
Solar Systems Inc., 507 W. Elm, Tyler, TX 75702
Thermon Mfg. Co., 100 Thermon Dr., San Marcos, TX 78666
United Electric Co., Magic Aire Div., P.O. Box 5148, Wichita Falls, TX 76307

Utah
Permalloy Corp., 2861 S. 1100 W., Ogden, UT 84402

Vermont
Appropriate Technology Corp., 14 Green St., Brattleboro, VT 05301
Enertech Corp., River Rd., Norwich, VT 05055
North Wind Power Co., Box 315, Warren, VT 05674
Sam Daniels Co., Inc., Box 868, Montpelier, VT 05602
Solar Alternative, Inc., 22 S. Main, Brattleboro, VT 05301

Virginia
Artech Corp., 2901 Telestar Ct., Falls Church, VA 22042
Corillium Corp., 11800 Sunrise Valley Dr., Reston, VA 22090
Helios Corp., 1313 Belleview Ave., Charlottesville, VA 22901
Intertechnology/Solar Corp., 100 Main St., Warrenton, VA 22186
Martin Processing, Inc., P.O. Box 5068, Martinsville, VA 24112
One Design, Inc., Mountain Falls Rt., Winchester, VA 22601
Pioneer Energy Products, Rte. 1, Box 189, Forest, VA 24551
Robertshaw Controls Co., 1800 Glenside Dr., P.O. Box 26542, Richmond, VA 23261

Washington
Floscan Instrument Co., Inc., 3016 NE Blakely St., Seattle, WA 98105
Mann-Russell Electronics, Inc., 1401 Thorne Rd., Tacoma, WA 98421
Sea-Lect Products, Inc., 807 S. Third, Kent, WA 98031
Small Hydroelectric Systems & Equipment, P.O. Box 124, Custer, WA 98240
Vertrex Corp., Suite 208, Carlson Bldg., 808 106th NE, Bellevue, WA 98004

Wisconsin
Ark-Tic-Seal Systems, Inc., P.O. Box 428, Butler, WI 53007
Dramm Corp., 2000 N. 18th St., Manitowoc, WI 54220
Erie Mfg. Co., 4000 S. 13th St., Milwaukee, WI 53221
Kickapoo Stove Works, Ltd., Main St., La Farge, WI 54639
Malleable Iron Range Co., Monarch Range and Heater Div., 715 N. Spring St., Beaver Dam, WI 53916
Silicon Sensors, Inc., Highway 18 E., Dodgeville, WI 53533

For a more complete and up-to-date list, write to ERDA Technical Information Center, Box 62, Oak Ridge, TN 37830, and ask for the catalog *Solar Heating and Cooling Products*, document number ERDA-75.

You may also write to the National Solar Heating and Cooling Information Center, P.O. Box 1607, Rockville, MD 20850. They have addresses of solar hot water equipment manufacturers. These are nationwide listings, broken down by state. They will, if you so request, send you a list of the manufacturers for your area only.

A general list of solar equipment manufacturers is contained in the publication *Energy Primer*, available for $5.50 (prepaid) from Whole Earth Truck Store, 558 Santa Cruz Ave., Menlo Park, CA 94025. This includes descriptions and evaluations of equipment sold by the companies listed.

The Solar Energy Institute of America, 1110 Sixth St., N.W., Washington, DC 20001 sells the *Solar Energy Sourcebook* for $12, covering companies that manufacture equipment and companies providing technical services related to solar energy. If you join the institute the book is free, as are continual updates (the book is in the form of a loose-leaf binder).

For $8 you can buy a similar book, *Solar Industry Index*, from the Solar Energy Industries Association, 1001 Connecticut Ave. N.W., Washington, DC 20036. This book is updated annually, but you must buy the new version each year.

For a list of architects, engineers, and designers with experience in solar heating and cooling, see *The Solar Home Book*, by Bruce Anderson, in the preceding section of this Appendix.

# SOLAR ENERGY INFORMATION CENTERS

Many government agencies have been ordered to do work in the area of solar energy and to make information on the subject available to the public. You don't have to contact each individual agency to get information, as information centers have been established to send you publications put out by the agencies. Write and ask for whatever the centers can send you. Also ask to be put on their mailing lists for new publications concerning solar energy, catalogs, or anything else they want to send you. You may never again have to face an empty mailbox.

ERDA Technical Information Center. Box 62, Oak Ridge, TN 37830.
National Solar Heating and Cooling Information Center. P.O. Box 1607, Rockville, MD 20850. Or call toll-free (800) 523-2929; in Pennsylvania, (800) 462-4983; in Hawaii and Alaska, (800) 523-4700.
Solar Energy Research Institute. 1536 Cole Blvd., Golden CO 80401.
Consumer Information Center. Pueblo, CO 81009. Not a solar energy center exclusively, but their catalog includes many booklets on the subject. See the first section of this Appendix for examples.

## OTHER INFORMATION SOURCES

This is a brief list of other information sources. Various government agencies have useful information connected with the general topic of energy use and conservation. Since they do not deal only with solar energy, the agencies' publications are not always available through the centers listed in the preceding section. Also, some private organizations can provide information on solar energy and related topics; however, private groups provide less for free than the government agencies do. In both cases, you can write for catalogs and ask to be put on mailing lists.

Environmental Action Reprint Service. 2239 East Colfax, Denver, CO 80206.
International Compendium. 10762 Tucker St., Beltsville, MD 20705.
Solar Energy Services. P.O. Box 2166, Hendersonville, NC 28739.
National Center for Appropriate Technology. P.O. Box 3838, Butte, MT 59701.
Federal Energy Administration. Office of Consumer Affairs/

Special Impact, 12th and Pennsylvania Ave., N.W., Room 4310, Washington, DC 20461.

Community Services Administration. The CSA operates offices called Community Action Agencies in various cities; there may be one near you. In some cities the name is not Community Action Agency, so you may not be able to track them down. Try writing to the head office—Community Services Administration, Washington, DC 20506—and ask for the address of the office nearest you.

Office of Public Affairs, Federal Energy Administration. Washington, DC 20461.

National Association of Home Builders Research Foundation, Inc. P.O. Box 1627, Rockville, MD 20850.

National Mineral Wool Association. 382 Springfield Ave., Summit, NJ 07901. Information on mineral wool insulation.

National Cellulose Insulation Manufacturers Association. 400 W. Madison St., Chicago, IL 60606. Information on cellulose insulation.

Architectural Aluminum Manufacturers Association. 35 East Wacker, Chicago, IL 60611. Information on storm doors and windows.

# INDEX

# Index

Consumer Information Center, 185
CONSUMER REPORTS' MONEY SAVING GUIDE TO ENERGY IN THE HOME (Consumers Union), 128, 182
Consumers Union, CONSUMER REPORTS' MONEY-SAVING GUIDE TO ENERGY IN THE HOME, 128, 182
continental shelf, 23
cooling, solar, 82–89
Crowther, Richad L., SUN, WIND, EARTH, 100, 182

Daniels, Farrington, DIRECT USE OF SUN'S ENERGY, 75, 181, 182
Daniels, George, SOLAR HOMES AND SUN HEATING, 81, 182
Davey, E. T., SOLAR WATER HEATING, 75
DESIGN FOR A LIMITED PLANET (Norma Skurka and John Naar), 42, 159, 183
DIRECT USE OF SUN'S ENERGY (Farrington Daniels), 75, 181
Doctrine of Ancient Lights, 167–69
"Drumwall" design, 155

EARTH, WATER, WIND AND SUN: OUR ENERGY ALTERNATIVE (D. S. Halacy, Jr.), 41, 181
economics of solar energy, 129–40
Einstein, Albert, 160–61
ENERGY (John Holdren and Philip Herrera), 41, 181
energy companies, 22
energy crisis, 17
energy-efficient home design, 90–101
ENERGY FOR SURVIVAL (Wilson Clark), 41, 75, 180
energy intensiveness of basic materials, 57
ENERGY OR EXTINCTION? THE CASE FOR NUCLEAR ENERGY (Fred Hoyle), 41, 182
ENERGY PRIMER (Whole Earth Truck Store), 184
English common law, 167
Environmental Action Foundation, 23
Environmental Action Reprint Service, 185

ERDA Technical Information Center, SOLAR HEATING AND COOLING PRODUCTS, 184, 185
Eskimos, 91
Exxon, 22

Faraday, Michael, 83
Federal Energy Administration, 186
  BUYING SOLAR, 139, 150
  Office of Public Affairs, 186
flat plate solar collector, 51–54, 59
Florida Solar Energy Center, 145, 148
food chain, 18
fossil fuels, 13, 18–20
Foster, William H., HOME-OWNER'S GUIDE TO SOLAR HEATING AND COOLING, 140, 181
free standing collector, 65, 66
free standing heat storage tank, 65
"Freon," 84
Fresnel Lens, 45, 47
Fuller, John G., WE ALMOST LOST DETROIT, 41, 182

General Electric, 144
General Motors, 144, 150
geography and solar energy, 106–18
geothermal power, 13, 30
Glauber's Salt, 64
government controls, 22
Gulf Coast Indians, 91

Halacy, Jr., D.S., EARTH, WATER, WIND AND SUN: OUR ENERGY ALTERNATIVE, 41, 181
Hartford, Washington, 34
Harrisburg, Pennsylvania, 32
Hay, Harold (house of), 153, 155, 157
Hayes, Denis, RAYS OF HOPE, 41, 181
heating, solar:
  home, 76–81
  water, 67–75
heating degree days, 115
heating load, 115
Herrera, Philip. *See co-author* John Holdren
Holdren, John and Philip Herrera, ENERGY, 41, 181
home cooling, 82–89, 98
home design, 90–101

199

# Index

# Index

Romans, 91

Ruffner, James A. and Frank E. Bair (eds.), THE WEATHER ALMANAC, 118, 183

Scortia, Thomas M. and Frank M. Robinson, THE PROMETHEUS CRISIS, 42, 183

Seri-Solar Energy Research Institute, 144, 185

shade control, 168

simple solar space heating system, 78

simplified absorption cycle cooling system, 86

Skurka, Norma, and John Naar, DESIGN FOR A LIMITED PLANET, 42, 159, 183

Skylab, 160

*Solar Age* (magazine), 75

solar cells, 160–65

Solar energy:
added to existing homes, 102–105
conservation and, 119–28
consumerism and, 141–50
current situation of, 17–42
economics of, 24, 129–40
geography and, 106–18
legal aspects of, 166–78
political aspects of, 166–78
solar cells and, 160–65
unconventional, 151–59
understanding, 43–66

Solar Energy Industries Association, SOLAR INDUSTRY INDEX, 143, 184

Solar Energy Institute of America, SOLAR ENERGY SOURCEBOOK, 184

Solar Energy Research Institute, 144, 185

SOLAR ENERGY SOURCEBOOK (Solar Energy Institute of America), 184

Solar Energy Services, 186

Solar Energy System, 65

SOLAR HEATING AND COOLING (Jan F. Kreider and Frank Kreith), 75, 101, 140, 182

SOLAR HEATING AND COOLING PRODUCTS (ERDA Technical Information Center), 184

SOLAR HOME BOOK, THE (Bruce Anderson), 100, 159, 180, 184

solar homes:
conversion to, 102–105
cooling of, 82–89
economics of, 24, 129–40
energy saving in, 90–101
design of, 90–101
heating of, 76–81
location of, 106–18
solar cells and, 160–65
unconventional, 151–59
water heating in, 67–75

SOLAR HOMES AND SUN HEATING (George Daniels), 81

SOLAR HOT WATER AND YOUR HOME (National Solar Heating and Cooling Information Center), 75

SOLAR HOT WATER HEATERS YOU CAN BUY NOW (Richard Stepler), 75

"Solar Hot Water Heating" (D. Mahone), 75

SOLAR HOMES AND SUN HEATING (George Daniels), 182

SOLAR INDUSTRY INDEX (Solar Energy Industries Index Association), 184

SOLAR LAW (Sandy F. Kramer), 178, 182

Solar One (University of Delaware), 164

solar powered, 14

solar space heating system, 78

solar water heater in heat exchange, 74

SOLAR WATER HEATING (E. T. Davey), 75

solarized house, 14

South Africa, 51

Southern California, 68

South Seas natives, 91

space heating, 76

Stein, Richard G., ARCHITECTURE AND ENERGY, 101, 183

Stepler, Richard, SOLAR HOT WATER HEATERS YOU CAN BUY NOW, 75

SUN! A HANDBOOK FOR THE SOLAR DECADE (Stephen Lyon, ed.), 41, 181

SUN, WIND, EARTH (Richard L. Crowther), 100, 182

sunlight by latitude, 107

sunshine, hours of, 108–12, 116

# Index

terminology, 14
theory of relativity, 161
Third World, 89
Three Mile Island, 32, 33
tidal power, 13
TIPS FOR CONSUMERS IN-
SULATING THEIR HOMES
(U.S. Government), 128, 183
TIPS FOR ENERGY SAVERS (U.S.
Department of Energy), 128, 183
TRAVELING WEATHERWISE IN
THE U.S.A. (Edward and James
Witt), 117, 183

U.S. Constitution, 177
U.S. Defense Department, 20
U.S. Department of Energy, TIPS
FOR ENERGY SAVERS, 144
U.S. Department of Housing and
Urban Development, IN THE
BANK OR UP THE CHIMNEY,
182
U.S. Department of Labor, 32
U.S. Government, TIPS FOR CON-
SUMERS INSULATING
THEIR HOMES, 128, 183
U.S. Weather Bureau, 113

University of Delaware, 164

vapor-compression cycle cooling system, 84

water based solar energy collection
and storage system, 61
WE ALMOST LOST DETROIT
(John G. Fuller), 33, 41, 182
WEATHER ALMANAC, THE
(James A. Ruffner and Frank
Bair), 118, 183
Western civilization, 13
Western states, 29
Whole Earth Truck Store, 184
wind power, 13
window awnings, 98
winters in the 1970s, 20
Witt, James. See co-author Edward
Powers
World War III, 35
Wright, David, NATURAL SOLAR
ARCHITECTURE: A PAS-
SIVE PRIMER, 101, 183

Yarosh, Marvin, 145

Zomeworks Corporation, 158